Mike Monteiro

YOU'RE MY FAVORITE CLIENT

Publisher: Jeffrey Zeldman
Designer: Jason Santa Maria
Managing Director: Katel LeDû
Editor: Tina Lee
Copyeditor: Nicole Fenton
Proofreader: Nadxi Nieto
Compositor: Rob Weychert
Editorial Assistant: Sally Kerrigan
Ebook Producer: India Amos

ISBN 978-1-937557-14-0

A Book Apart
New York, New York
http://abookapart.com

10 9 8 7 6 5 4 3 2 1

TABLE OF CONTENTS

FOREWORD

AS MUCH AS YOU think you know a man, I suspect you'd know a great deal more if you could meet his mother. Mike is the son of a seamstress. Judite Monteiro's specialty is wedding dresses, and young Mike watched firsthand as she worked with brides to get the right pattern, the right fabric, the right fit. "As a kid, I was getting a master lesson in client services," he writes. "A lesson on how to...work *with* a client instead of *for* a client." Later on, Mike discovered that "the way a seamstress approaches her craft isn't too far off from a designer."

Here we get to the point: design disasters usually spring from the faulty notion that design is *art* not *craft*. Mike's first book, *Design Is A Job,* gave designers a swift kick in the pants, admonishing them to wake up, ditch their artsy-fartsy egos, and take responsibility for their work. In this new book, Mike demystifies design for non-designers, showing them that good design isn't the product of "creatives" pulling rabbits from a magical hat but a rigorous process of problem solving, performed by professionals.

If you are a designer, buy this book and give it to your clients—but also to the designers you know to remind them of the good work you're all trying to do.

If you are a client, feel confident that whoever handed you this book cares about making your collaboration work. Read it, learn from it, and buy a copy for your colleagues so they can learn from it too.

For client services to succeed, both the craftsperson and the client must take responsibility for their roles. This book will help you play your part in getting the work done, whether you're the seamstress or the bride.

—**Austin Kleon**

Dedicated to Leslie Harpold, who taught me how to write a thank you note.

INTRODUCTION

"I DON'T KNOW anything about design."

Bullshit.

Look around you. You make choices based on design every day. The chair you're probably enjoying now is designed to make you feel comfortable. The clothes you choose to wear are designed to make you feel confident or relaxed (or both), depending on the day of the week. The car you drive is designed to make you feel safe, unless it's designed to make you feel young. But you know the difference.

Even if you can't design those things yourself, that doesn't take away from your ability to decide that was the chair you wanted to sit on, or the shoes you wanted to wear, or the car you wanted to buy.

You make design decisions every day.

You've designed things to achieve your goals since you were a kid, from diagramming a sandlot football play in the dirt to sussing out how to play your parents against each other to land a trip to Disneyland. You're very capable of stating your goal and knowing whether you've achieved it. And when you achieve your goal, you say your plan has gone "as designed."

That's it: design is the plan that gets us to our goal.

You know a lot more about design than you give yourself credit for.

You know bad design when you encounter it. From every chair you've sat in that hurt your ass, to every coffee cup that burned your hand, to every time your finger triggered the wrong link on your phone, to every airline booking site that pissed you off. You know bad design. You hate it. And you should. Because anything designed poorly could've been designed better. The truth is that good design isn't magic: it takes a clear goal, the expertise and resources to reach that goal, and, most of all, the intention to do it well.

As smart as you are about design (and you are! Go read from the beginning if you don't yet believe it), sometimes the goals you're trying to achieve need the services of someone who designs solutions for a living. People trained to solve problems. The difference between being design savvy, which many people are—including yourself—and having design skills is experience honed over time. We may all appreciate a nice pair of shoes, but few of us can actually make them.

As with any profession, you have good designers, bad designers, and designers that aren't right for you. Designers—I'm one of them—can be difficult to work with. It can be intimidating to search for design services without a playbook.

Congratulations. You're holding the playbook for hiring design services!

I've been in the design business a long time. I run an interactive design shop called Mule Design in San Francisco, and I hear this phrase from my clients almost every day: "I don't know anything about design." I love my clients. They help me keep the lights on. They're good people, and they all have one thing in common: they showed up with a goal in mind. My job is to add my design expertise to their business expertise and design a solution that accomplishes their goal. I love doing it. I want to help you love it too.

No one is born knowing how to be a good client. (I certainly wasn't born a good designer.) Successful design projects need equal participation from the client and the designer. Yet the design process remains a mystery to the people who buy it. Design isn't sausage. You'll enjoy it even more if you understand how it's made. This book will attempt to demystify that process *and* help you prepare for your role. Well-informed clients make projects run more smoothly and effectively, and well-run projects ultimately cost less. This book will help you ask the right questions, get the right answers, and work with the right people. You'll have the confidence to hire people who challenge you to make your product the best it can be.

When you hire a designer, you're not hiring a pair of hands. You're hiring a mind that's been trained to solve problems in a way you can't.

Design isn't magic and it isn't art. It's a craft. Design solves a problem within a set of given constraints. We'll talk about why those constraints matter. Much as a doctor needs patients to practice *their* craft, a designer needs clients to practice theirs. Like walking into a doctor's office, describing what's wrong, and then having your doctor diagnose the problem and prescribe a solution, working with a designer is the same. You tell us what's wrong, and we research, come up with a plan, and design a solution. We don't ask for blind trust, but we do ask that you respect that we've been trained in handling a scalpel. And maybe a *little* trust.

Why should you trust me? That's easy. I have selfish reasons for writing this book. One, prepared clients make my job easier. The less time we spend debating whether design's important, the more time we spend making design better. Two, I work with clients who've had terrible experiences with designers who, for whatever reason, did a crap job. So I end up taking time to rebuild their trust. Again, that's time we could spend making better design. Three, I love my craft. I want to make sure it's practiced right. I have little patience for designers misrepresenting our capabilities and responsibilities to clients.

A well-designed world is a better world. I love knowing that a thoughtful piece of user interface makes someone's life go a bit easier, whether it's designing a menu that's accessible to someone with low vision or watching my seventy-one-year-old father intuitively use an iPad for the first time. Good design has the power to change lives in big *and* small ways.

Writing this book is one of those cases when doing the right thing also makes good business sense. Win-win.

If you've never worked with a designer before, this book will demystify how to hire the right designer, what to expect from them, and how to work collaboratively to ensure your project's success. (Also how to handle the situation should it go south.)

If you've worked with a designer, you'll find out how to communicate more effectively, why giving them detailed lists of what to do doesn't get you their best work, and why hovering over their shoulder drives them nuts. You'll find out why designers belong in the strategy meeting. You'll find out design starts way before a pixel gets pushed or a line gets drawn.

To any designers reading this book: I'm here to help you too. Many clients have never bought design services. Don't assume your clients come to the table knowing what you need to make the process go well. Feel free to use this book to introduce new clients to the design process. The more your clients know what's needed to make a project, the more successful you'll both be. Give a copy to everyone who walks through your door! A few caveats. My company designs websites, apps, and other digital interactive stuff. Most of my examples come from that experience. But even if you're designing books, tables, or hadron colliders, these lessons apply. (If you're designing hadron colliders, please make sure to read a second book.) Also, I'm in client services. I'm someone your company hires to augment or serve in place of an internal team. I've spent a lot of time working in-house, so this book has plenty to help you work with designers in any situation.

When I say designers, I mean the people who participate in the design of your websites, apps, and atom smashers: visual designers, interaction designers, content strategists, researchers, developers, and new roles we'll invent by tomorrow. We'll dig deeper into what *design* means. Yes, the definitive definition!

Pack a lunch. We've got work to do. Leave your wands behind. Beyond this page, there is no magic. Only real talk.

(I'm kidding. There's a picture of a unicorn in Chapter 6.)

1

WHY YOU NEED DESIGN

WHAT IS DESIGN?

Design results from human decisions. You can design with intention, which means you have a chance of doing it well, or you can let it happen, which means you'll probably bungle the job. Design happens whether you're aware you're doing it or not paying attention. Nothing is undesigned. Things are badly designed, well designed, and points between.

What do I mean by *design?* Design is how we communicate what an object does, or its function, through its shape or form.

Take a baseball mitt. Study it for a bit, and it becomes obvious that your hand goes inside. That's form. The minute you have the mitt on, you understand it makes it easier to catch a baseball. That's function.

Design is also the process we undertake to solve a problem. It fucking hurts to catch a baseball with your bare hand. A mitt is the solution to that problem.

If you ask five designers to define design, you'll get five different answers. For our purposes, and because we have actual work to do, the above definition works fine.

Let's revisit our chair example. When you think about the design of a chair, you consider both how it looks and how it feels to sit on. A well-designed office chair corrects your posture and enhances your productivity, while a well-designed living room chair lets you lie back and relax, watch TV, play with your iPad, and take a nap. An airline seat is purposely designed to fill you with regret and levels of sadness unknown in human history outside the Spanish Inquisition.

If you and I were to design a chair together, we'd have to consider some factors from the get-go. Of course, we'd consider the seat's size, the height from the ground, the angle of the back, the materials, and the fabric. Before we made any of those decisions, we'd ask ourselves about the chair's goals. Who would be using the chair? What would they be doing? How would the chair benefit the person sitting in it? These answers affect how we communicate its function. When a person's expectation of the chair matches their experience of sitting in the chair, they get more joy out of it. This is design done right.

Will those considerations ensure that the chair is well designed? No, but they certainly increase the odds. *Not* thinking about them ensures that our chair is *badly* designed.

Yet when we build websites or apps, we often wait until the last minute to bring in designers to "apply" design, or look and feel. This is akin to baking a cake and *then* hiring a baker to make it taste good. (We've mixed our first metaphor!)

WHAT'S DESIGN'S VALUE?

Imagine two chair shops across the street from each other. One shop takes the chair's design into consideration from the start. They hire the best chair designer they can. The chair designer researches other chairs on the market to figure out where they're lacking. They ask people what they like and dislike about their current chairs, research materials, consider the chair company's budget and profit margin, and source materials and manufacturing to make sure the chair is built right. They test different designs. They make adjustments. They test again. They come up with a solid design that meets both the company's goals and people's desires. The chair goes into production. It sells well. Everyone is now rich.

The people at the chair shop across the street also make a chair. They select adequate materials and make a seat, some legs, a back. This is definitely a chair! Then they hire a designer and say, "Make this a comfortable chair!" The designer adds a sad little foam rubber seat cushion. The chair bombs. Everyone dies of dysentery.

The value of good design is the increased possibility of success. We understand its importance in everyday objects like chairs, clothes, watches, coffee makers, and a good mattress. When it comes to websites, we tend to think of design as a surface layer applied at the end. In truth, that website's design started long ago. It can be intentional or happenstance. For design to be truly great, you need to build it into your projects from conception. Because if you're not doing it, you can bet your competitors are.

To get design's full value, you need to hire a professional. You need a designer. Would you trust any other valuable part of your business to someone who wasn't qualified to do it? Would you let your cousin's best friend do your accounting because they had a calculator? Or let your neighbor reprogram your fuel injection system because they have three cars on blocks on their lawn? Probably not.

We hire professionals because we can hold them accountable. If you get audited, you better believe you're taking your accountant with you to the hearing. If the credit card processing system on your site goes down, you want to know that your engineering team is on it. You also want to be able to call them into your office and ask what happened. When your users can't figure out your site's interface, you want to know you've got people trained in designing effective interfaces on the job. When you ask people to take on tasks that are neither part of their job nor something they're trained at, you have no right to complain if they screw it up. Gift horses and whatnot.

Can I guarantee that hiring a professional designer will result in good design? No more than a college can guarantee that studying there will make you smarter. But it certainly improves your odds. Especially if you find the right fit. We'll go over that in a bit.

Look for thoughtful, inventive problem solvers with excellent communication skills. Don't get dazzled by the "creatives" trap. If you catch yourself thinking, "We could really use some of this energy around here," put down the Kool-Aid. Treat your designers (and call them *designers*) as adult professionals. Hold them responsible for measurable job performance goals, the same as other employees.

WHAT DESIGN CAN'T FIX

Let me tell you a story that's playing out among every media company in the world. The editorial team is arguing to make their website look more modern, offer a cleaner reading experience with better typography, and hey, while we're at it, let's kill pagination. Across the table, the sales team is arguing for their ad units, for placement above the fold. (The concept of a fold will outlive every newspaper on the planet.) They're arguing for three or four or five ad units on every page. To be fair, their job effectiveness is measured by those units. While I'm generally (always) on the editorial team's side, I empathize with the sales team as well.

This isn't unlike Stringer Bell pushing for the co-op as Avon Barksdale screams back, "I *want* my corners!" (This is the first reference to *The Wire*. Won't be the last. Be ready. Everyone in business should watch *The Wire*.)

So the company hires a design team to help solve their problem. If the design team's good, they'll tell the truth: the problem is that the stakeholders have different goals. The site can't solve the problem, because the two sides need to agree over the conference table first. Otherwise, they're passing a compromised intent to readers.

In our experience as a design firm, it's common for client team members to disagree among themselves. They get to the point where some people want one thing like exposed navigation, and others want it hidden. They ask us to devise a solution that meets both teams halfway. Or someone higher up has a

FIG 1: The El Camino: manifestation of compromised intent. Photograph by Useute, English Wikipedia Project (http://bkaprt.com/ymfc/1/).

drastically different reaction to the work than the core project team. So they ask us to design something that tricks the CEO while staying the course. Or worse: "Can you show us both variations to help us make up our minds?"

The answer is no.

As my good friend Jared Spool says, "Design is the rendering of intent" (http://bkaprt.com/ymfc/2/). When the intent isn't clear, the project stakeholders can't agree on goals, or two founders veer in two directions to take their company, no amount of design can solve that situation. Design doesn't work if you don't know your intent. Otherwise, you'll find yourself in the land of mullets, half-cafs, cran-grape drinks, platypuses, and El Caminos (FIG 1). (Granted, platypuses are pretty cool. But they're filled with poison.)

Designers can design a solution to a problem, but they can't design a solution to a disagreement. Some designers try to apply the wisdom of Solomon by coming up with a solution so terrible the disagreeing parties have no choice but to finally agree. This never works. And they soon find themselves breathing life into Frankenstein's monster. A designer should never put something in front of you they don't stand by.

Before you commit to the design process, make sure your goals are clear and your team's on board with those core goals. Bring in the designer once you've done so. Bring them in to help you work through the details and the strategy, and then leave the solutions up to the designer.

The only way out from unclear goals is to talk through them until you've achieved clarity of intention. (Pro tip: do this in a room with no windows and no chairs that also smells like eggs. You'll cut your time in half.)

Here's a handy list of problems you may need to solve before spending precious time and money on design.

Imaginary business model

One of the first questions I ask potential clients is how they'll make money with the thing they want me to design. Everyone (hopefully) remembers the underpants gnomes episode of *South Park*. The gnomes have a foolproof plot to get rich:

Phase 1: Collect underpants
Phase 2: ??
Phase 3: Profit!

That's right. It's the exact plan we used to build the internet! The lovable rapscallions of *South Park* couldn't help the underpants gnomes execute their plan and were wary of giving up their underpants without knowing the purpose.

You can't design a system for profit unless you understand where that profit comes from. At the least, you can't design it well. To tell whether something is designed well, you need clear metrics. One such metric should be whether the business model is successful, if you want to stick around. With a clear and reasonable business model, you have a chance at a successful design.

Here's an example that doesn't involve gnomes. Say you hire a designer and your business model is ad-driven. The designer does an excellent job optimizing the ad spots to generate revenue and places them where advertisers will pay a premium. Two weeks after launch, you decide your most important metric for success isn't ad revenue but the number of newsletter subscribers, which was a low priority during the redesign. You look at the number of newsletter subscriptions, and it's a weak number. Does that mean the site wasn't designed correctly? No. That's the site working as designed. When your business model shifts, you need a redesign—so hammer out your business goals before you start.

Bad content

Since we're becoming friends I'll tell you a secret. No one comes to a site because of the design. They come for the content or the service, like booking air travel. The design should encourage them to stay, offering a wonderfully easy-to-understand and even delightful way to interact with that content or service. Bad design can certainly bury good content, but you can't design a "premium experience" and pour crap content into it with any expectation of success.

A few years ago, I had the pleasure of working with *ProPublica* (http://bkaprt.com/ymfc/3/), a team of investigative journalists who do incredible work. Their initial strategy was to partner with newspapers (many of whom had laid off their own investigative reporters) and publish stories through these partners. *ProPublica* intentionally focused their resources on reporting rather than their website. Over time, the pool of available partners dwindled, and *ProPublica* realized they needed to create a suitable platform to publish their work. We were lucky enough that they chose to partner with us. Our job was relatively easy. All we had to do was create an effective showcase to highlight that work. These days *ProPublica* is gobbling up Pulitzers like Pez. Is this because of the site design? No. But the design makes reading their stories a more pleasant experience.

It's all about content, people. Design is what holds it together. So before you drop a chunk of money and time on design, get some writers and content strategists. And beware of people who talk about "consuming content." No one has ever woken up with the desire to consume content in their life.

A lack of resources

The first part of our design process is what we call the discovery phase. This is when we examine every aspect of the design problem. We talk to people in the organization. We talk to your users, discuss your goals, and find out how you get things done. Only after we've done this research can we think about how to solve anything. Most studios have a similar research phase. Be leery of those that don't.

The most crucial thing we discover is how you work as a team. We need to know how many people actively publish to or maintain the website, and how much time they commit to it. We also need to know their skill sets. Any decent design solution takes your resources into account.

So when a client says, "We want tons of big photos," my next question is, "Who's going to source those?" When we don't have a clear answer, or when the indicated individual lacks the skill set (and sourcing photography *is* a skill), the website will probably fail. The same applies to infographics, only it's ten times worse.

If I design a system that you lack the resources to sustain, I'm not doing *my* job. I haven't designed a solution to the problem; I've *created* a problem. A good designer can't in good conscience deliver something to a client knowing it will fail.

Be wary of gravitating toward a design that calls for a nonexistent resource. On the plus side, you could become a job creator!

Stealth stakeholder

"They'll come around when they see what great work you're doing." Sure they will. They'll come around and kill the project because they've been left out of it.

I've unfortunately gotten myself into this position a few times. A well-meaning team hires me. I ask if all the stakeholders are aware of the project. They say, "Yes," or more likely, "Sure!" We proceed, do a ton of great work together, and when the project's about to go live, a previously invisible stakeholder emerges from the shadows like Batman. The specter sometimes manifests as: "We need to get the board's approval before final sign-off." Replace board with *investor, dean, silent partner, dad...* you get the idea.

No work is so good that it makes people happy they were left out. As difficult as the conversation or logistics may be to get those people on board before the project begins, I guarantee you (and I'll give you few guarantees in this book) *that* conversation is easier than the conversation when they realize they're out of the loop.

So before you scope the project or interview designers, ask yourself, "Who can kill this project?" Involve that person! Make an ally, not an enemy. Include your designer in the conversation. I'd much rather help you convince your CEO at the project's onset than stand in her office three-quarters of the way through the project to explain how I've been spending her money.

Conflicted chain of command

Nothing halts a design project like hazy direction or contradictory client feedback. As I mentioned at the start of this chapter, we often get conflicting feedback from clients who haven't sorted out their priorities.

Clients ideally handle internal disagreement before feedback reaches the designer, but since hearing the source of the disagreement is often instructive, I'm okay with not drawing a hard line and hearing what the disagreement is about.

When the feedback contradicts itself, our job is to point that out and help the client clarify and prioritize. Someone on the client side may have to step up and make the ultimate call. We need to know who has the final say, which means you need to know first.

Let me tell you about Larry. Larry is one of my all-time favorite clients. (Unseating Larry should be your goal.) Anyway, Larry had a team of bright, opinionated people. I loved working with them. During one of our early meetings, everyone was arguing a point I've long since forgotten, but the opinions were flying around pretty fast and Larry was sitting there listening. Mulling things over.

At one point, someone made a fairly impassioned case and Larry shouted, "Sold!"

The argument continued.

Larry, in a friendly, authoritative voice, said, "You don't understand. When I say 'Sold,' it means that you've convinced me and the discussion is over."

In that moment, there was absolutely no confusion about the chain of command. I've since adopted yelling, "Sold!" during our own internal meetings, much to my team's dismay.

WHAT'S A DESIGNER?

"Bring in the creatives!"

When most people think of designers, they picture something exotic. A rule-breaker! A free spirit. They may picture Edna Mode from *The Incredibles* forcing her newly designed suits on a freaked-out Elastigirl. They may see Stan from *Mad Men* lighting a joint in the office. Or Will Ferrell's character Mugatu from *Zoolander.* And god bless those of you imagining Darrin Stephens from *Bewitched,* who was unable to solve a client's problem without the intervention of forbidden wife-magic.

We've been trained to think of designers as people who are a few cards short of a tarot deck, out in left field, creatures of instinct. They don't follow rules. They accidentally set conference rooms on fire. And they only work when inspiration rolls up for a visit. Even worse, we believe that those are the qualities we should value and seek out in designers.

The myth of inspiration has a strong hold on designers and their clients. Both share in its perpetuation. (Can you imagine letting any other employee get away with only working when inspired? I hope not.)

The world of advertising, whose list of sins runs deep, has sinned most by branding these people as *creatives,* which the world of web design sadly adopted as its own. Calling someone a creative doesn't elevate. It marginalizes. The label excludes designers from conversations about strategy, product definition, business goals, and metrics. It sets them apart from other employees as people who aren't bound by the same expectations and requirements. It diminishes their opportunity to be seen as people capable of analytical, rigorous thought.

Saddest of all, people who went on to become designers grew up with those stereotypes and adopted them as their own. This is why you have people self-identifying as creatives. Coming into work when they please. Skipping requirements meetings. Blathering about inspiration while the money you're paying them is flushed down the toilet, along with your deadlines.

And here I am telling you to hire these people.

Except I'm not. I want to redraw your mental picture of a designer and tell you what you *should* expect of them.

I'm here to say it's okay to tell them to take off the stupid panda hat at work.

A good designer behaves like a skilled professional with analytical, persuasive, creative, and social skills. You can count on them to solve problems, present good work in a timely manner, be accountable, and argue from an informed point of view.

Designers aren't artists. Design isn't self-expression. Nothing special or magical marks design. While designers come in many flavors, some bitter and some with a lemony aftertaste, don't tolerate any of those flavors if the designers don't behave professionally.

Let's explore the vast world of designers and learn more about what they do and what you should expect.

Designers make things

This is probably the part you already associate with designers: the making of the thing. Yes, with the mockups (don't call them mocks!), the layouts, and the coding. I won't spend too much of your time here, except to emphasize that the reason this part works is all the attention to the parts that come before it: the research and the strategy. Understanding the problem. Heck, sitting down to execute is almost the easy part if you did the prep work.

Designers solve problems

Once upon a time, I did a research interview with a young designer who worked at a big company. I asked him at what point he got involved in projects. He told me that the product team, the management team, and the engineering team—basically everyone but him—got together and defined the product strategy. They wrote product specs, made wireframes, did most everything but tie a bow on the project, and handed it over to "design." I asked this kid, and he was a good kid, why he didn't attend those meetings. He said he wasn't invited. (Small aside to any designer reading: don't wait for an invite. Get your ass in there. Your boss may not even know it's important for you to be present. I'm about to tell them, but part of your job is knowing where you need to be and telling people you need to be there.)

You hire designers to help solve your problem. To do so to the best of their abilities, designers need to take part in conversations where everyone discusses the problem and bandies about solutions. This helps them better understand what you're asking them to do, and it puts people in the room who may have a different approach to the problem. You want as many diverse points of view as possible. If you're worried about bringing a designer into the room because you're batting around half-baked ideas, that's exactly why the designer should be there: to throw in ingredients you wouldn't think of and keep you from fully baking the bad ones.

Design starts with understanding the problem and helping to set the strategy. Not having your designer participate in the problem solving is like a restaurant investor handing the daily menu to the chef and saying, "Make this." Neither of us would want to eat at that restaurant.

And, yes, if you have a designer who hasn't asked to be involved as early as possible, you should be a little worried.

Designers advocate for your users

Your success depends on how well your product or service meets the needs of the people who use it, and how many people you get to use it. Good designers understand this. They find out who your customers are, how they behave, and how they think. Some designers even create personas to better represent these people so it's easier to plan and design with them in mind.

I once worked with a designer who bought frames with photos of strangers at thrift stores. She stashed the photos in a box under her desk. When she started a project, she flipped through them until she found people she felt matched the users we were designing for. She kept those frames on her desk for the project's duration to remind her that she wasn't designing for herself. She was designing for them.

Every good designer is a bit of a method actor. We try to design through the eyes of the people we anticipate using the product. Does this mean we disregard your business needs? Au contraire! We make sure that your business needs match the needs of the people you're trying to win over. Ultimately, that's the best thing we can do for your business.

Designers work well with others

It's almost impossible to design anything by yourself. It's also stupid. You improve everything when you talk to people with different viewpoints, experiences, and skill sets. The myth of the solitary genius is just that: a myth.

Design is a team sport. And a team with cohesive chemistry always beats a team with a few prima donna superstars. Even if the solitary genius manages to squeeze out a couple of good projects before everyone tires of their attitude, the door will eventually close on how long people are willing to put up with them.

A designer is a communication professional. When I start a project I get to know everyone on the client's team. I learn what they do, how they tick, how best to communicate with them; I develop relationships and trust. Projects take a while. You'll work together for a long time. You have information in your head that's crucial to the project's success, and I'm guessing you may not be quick to give it to someone who doesn't treat you with respect and kindness. You don't have to put up with the solitary genius *or* the asshole genius.

Designers have reasons

Designers need to be able to explain decisions in a rational manner and tie them to project goals. By letting you know how their solutions relate to research findings. By backing up their decisions with quotes from user interviews. By using data and analytics where applicable. They have to explain their decisions and do so convincingly. They have to sell it.

A designer who can't explain their rationale is useless—open to the whims and desires of everyone around them. If they don't understand their own decisions, they can't advocate for your users or replicate their choices across projects. They can't argue. Every designer in the world needs to be able to answer: "Why did you do that?" If their reply is, "I can change it," you're absolutely fucked.

"I think it looks good" is not a rationale. It's a red flag.

Designers take feedback and criticism

A solid, thoughtful rationale also nicely sets the table for good feedback. If your designer says they made a decision based on research and best practices, they're doing their job.

But a designer who says they were "inspired" to do something opens the door for a stakeholder to give feedback that's just as subjective. Whim begets whim. Now you've got a roomful of people arguing about their favorite colors.

But isn't inspiration important? Absolutely. Remember the scene in *Apollo 13* where the astronauts cobbled together random parts from around the ship to make an air purifier? Using everything at your disposal to meet a goal is inspiration. Throwing shit together and hoping it sticks isn't.

A designer confident in their decisions is confident enough to listen to criticism. They're showing you results based on systematic thought not a magical moment. People are more open to their math being wrong than having their fairy tales spoiled.

I've gone into presentations convinced that I was about to show a great solution. Fifteen minutes in, someone on the client team says, "You forgot to take x into account." And holy shit. They're right. At that point, my job is to shift gears and get everyone involved in solving for that case. And thank the awesome individual who uncovered it.

My friend Jared Spool, whom I've now quoted twice, says, "The best designers are passionate about design, but dispassionate about their own designs." (http://bkaprt.com/ymfc/4/). It's a good line. I wish I could take credit for it. (I eventually will.)

There's a big difference between defending work, which a designer must know how to do, and being defensive about work, which a designer should never do. When you point out an obvious problem to a designer and they keep fighting, they're no longer fighting for the work's quality. They're fighting for their ego. A good designer is confident enough to fight for what's right and acknowledge what's wrong.

Of course, you should make sure the criticism focuses on the work, not the person presenting the work. (We'll go into how to give good feedback in Chapter 4.)

How do you know if you have a good or bad designer? Let's find out.

RED FLAGS TO LOOK FOR IN DESIGNERS

- **Beware of designers who've only worked by themselves.** A designer who's worked alone only knows what they know. But a designer who's worked with other designers, taking in everything they had to teach, knows what they all know and isn't afraid to tell you what they need. A young kid who's the sole designer in a company founded by and filled with engineers or developers has a harder time learning how to make the case for their craft. They don't work to convince someone of a point, because they never feel like they have the backup. They're a pair of hired hands.
- **Beware of designers who wait for you to define their job.** The designer is the expert in what you hired them to do and what they need to get that done. After all, you hired them because they're uniquely qualified to do this. Good designers empower themselves to do their jobs. If you're in a situation where your designer asks for a lot of direction, you may need to remind them that you expect them to take charge of the things under their purview. Your designer should come to you for feedback that evaluates their proposed solution—but not direction, which asks you to come up with the solution itself. That's what you hired them for.

- **Beware designers who limit themselves to things they enjoy doing.** Let's be honest. No one in their right mind enjoys a requirements gathering meeting, but it helps get the job done. Anything that helps you do your job is part of your job. Combing through that information—and sharing in your teammates' pain of attending said meeting—makes the job's enjoyable parts more fruitful.
- **Beware a designer who doesn't ask questions.** I mean "Why are we doing it this way?" type questions, not "How do we do it?" questions. A designer, heck, everyone in your company, should be curious about why decisions are made the way they are. A good designer takes every decision apart to see if they can put it back together better. It's in every good designer's nature to improve what they're handed.
- **Beware a designer who doesn't argue from a strong point of view.** Once a designer is convinced that a specific choice is right, they should be willing to argue their position. They should also be open-minded enough to be proven wrong, but only if the opposing argument is strong enough to persuade them. Slight pushback shouldn't change their mind.
- **Beware a designer who wants you to like them more than they want to do good work.** Every designer has an aha moment in their career when they realize they're designing work the client hopes to see instead of work they know is right but needs a harder conversation to get the client's approval. Until they have that moment, they're not giving you their best work.

Your interactions with the designer go a long way in determining whether they're showing you their best work. You don't hire them to be your friend or to design to your own whims. You hire a designer to solve a problem. I've seen too many designers throw their research and good sense to the wind because the client expressed a personal preference and demanded they follow it. You don't want a designer who ends up doing the best work *you* can come up with. You want them designing the best work *they* can come up with.

Making the client happy is a by-product of doing good design. An excellent by-product, sure. But your happiness should never be the goal.

2
HIRING A DESIGNER

OKAY, YOU'RE SOLD on design. Once you're ready to hire a designer, decide if you need in-house or outside help. You can get good (and bad) design work out of either situation; your circumstances will dictate which is your best bet. Make sure you hire someone you trust and can spend the next few months or years with. Don't hire anyone you can't argue with or who's afraid of arguing with you. The road to good design has a few thorns—they breed character.

WHEN TO GET IN-HOUSE HELP

As I run a design shop that counts on clients hiring outside to stay in business, my next bit of advice may surprise you. If your organization produces anything on a continual basis, regularly communicates online with the public, or has a new product with quick revision cycles, you should absolutely, positively hire in house.

Not everyone can afford it, but make sure to consider it. If you're starting a new web service, for example, and you've hired twelve engineers and no designers, you're doing your future users (and your shareholders) a disservice.

The pros of in-house help:

- Their time is yours
- They're part of your culture
- They have relationships with the rest of your staff

The cons of in-house help:

- Their time is yours
- They're part of your culture
- They have relationships with the rest of your staff

Notice anything? Yeah, it's the same list.

An experienced in-house designer, given the right authority and possessing the right leadership qualities, establishes design's importance within your company. An in-house designer reflects your commitment to making something people want to use; this care will flow throughout the organization. You need someone with enough know-how to sell design to the rest of the company and the ability to rally people to a cause.

Weak in-house help may be worse than no help because it drapes you in the trappings of having a designer without the actual benefits. A designer who does everything they're told and lives in fear of your engineering or marketing team isn't doing their job.

A designer's work is only as good as their ability to sell it to you. By *sell,* I mean convince you. A designer may do excellent work that exceeds your stated goals, but if they can't convince you of that, the work is worthless. Design can be seen as a hopelessly subjective topic. It takes experience and confidence to understand how to sidestep the personal-opinion trap when presenting to others.

I hire young designers in my shop. They're talented but relatively new to the client services world, so they don't have a lot of experience with client feedback. Occasionally, we'll get feedback like, "Why did you use blue?" Within minutes, the designer swaps out blue for green.

If you ask a designer a clarifying question, and their immediate response is to reverse their decision, that's a red flag that they're uncomfortable with their choices or not confident enough in their ability to explain their decisions. Or they're scared of you! Whatever the reason, you're not getting their best work.

Most of the time a clarifying question is just that. "Why did you use blue?" is a fair question, one your designer should answer with confidence.

All that said, in-house help is the right solution for a lot of organizations. Especially if you need design on a consistent basis or you develop new products quickly. You'll want someone who gives you their undivided attention and establishes a culture where excellent design matters.

My advice is to hire someone at the design director level, particularly if you're hiring only one designer. This ensures you're hiring someone who has experience working with others and pushing design decisions through with the rest of the team. Hiring a senior role sends a signal that design matters to you. It also doesn't preclude you from hiring outside help later to augment your capabilities.

A design director will want to be all up in your strategy, which is exactly what they should do. If you can't afford someone at that level, you can still do well by hiring a midlevel designer who can hold their own most of the time. You can then hire more seasoned outside help to devise strategy on bigger projects as needed.

WHEN TO GET OUTSIDE HELP

Perhaps you can't afford to take on an internal salary, you have a specific project your team needs help with, or you need a fresh set of eyes on a problem. (Don't discount that last one.) Outside help is your best solution.

Consulting designers bring a clear perspective to the problem. Their experiences with other projects, even ones outside your industry, may shed new insight into what you're doing. People within your organization have deep knowledge about your particular situation (and sharing that with outside designers is crucial to your success), but a stranger's take on habitual circumstances may be the jolt everyone needs.

The biggest benefit of outside help is that they're not swimming in your organizational politics. As people coming in for the first time, they still get along with everyone! They don't have the history of that time Bob from Marketing pissed someone off by going over their head.

Since an outside designer is only passing through—and their salary and benefits aren't completely in your hands—they'll be more willing to argue with you, whereas your employees may be more reticent.

Outside help comes in a few flavors.

Freelancers

Freelancers are studios of one. You hire them for a set number of hours or a project fee. They come in, meet with you, and work in their own space. At the end, they send you an invoice. (Do me a favor and pay it in a timely fashion.) These people live job to job. Many are younger, starting out in their careers. They tend to be the most affordable option, great for small projects and budgets. Other freelancers are senior designers who value their independence. The difference between senior and junior generalists will be somewhat obvious in their portfolios, but unmistakeable in their communication with you.

Contractors

Contractors work in your space for a specified period of time or project. They're brought in when you need a skill set your team doesn't have or need full-time. (Remember Flash designers?!?) Some people, and I know you're not one of them, hire contractors and keep them around for years to avoid paying salaries and benefits. I know you don't do this, because it's illegal. Contractor laws vary like crazy, so please check with your lawyer. Some states have a threshold on how many months someone can be a contractor before the state decides they're an employee, regardless of how you classify them. I don't want you to get in trouble.

Contractors are great for taking on tasks you can't do in house, like data visualization or implementing a particular content management system. Even people like me who run design studios hire contractors from time to time. (We always notify our clients that we've brought in a contractor.) Specialty contractors also charge accordingly for that expertise.

Design studios

Design studios are a great option when you have a large project with defined goals and want the power of a multidisciplinary team that knows how to work together. Studios are typically made up of people with various levels of experience. The larger the studio, the more likely they've got a team that specializes in acquiring new projects, and another less-experienced team that'll do your work. Look behind the curtain and make sure you're talking to the people you're going to work with every day. (A bunch of big studios just blacklisted me for telling you that, so take it to heart.)

Most studios want you to bring them in early enough in the process to get a full understanding of the problem and help define the solution. Don't wait until you've "figured it out." A good design studio helps you devise solutions you haven't even thought of. They're gonna charge you for it anyway, so you may as well have them do the work.

At one point, agencies and studios differed, much like how streets and avenues probably aren't the same. I do want to note a major caveat. Some agencies out there are basically contractor farms, assembling teams on the fly from a giant rolodex of "talent." When you hire a team, make sure they've been through a few projects together and know how to complement one another without stepping on toes. You don't want a team thrown together at the last minute. (Perfect analogy for basketball fans: the first year LeBron James, Dwyane Wade, and Chris Bosh played together, they were an agency. After they learned how to complement each other they started winning championship rings. They became a studio.)

Another way to look at the whole thing: let's say you're building a backyard deck. You've decided to do most of the work yourself, but you need help carrying stuff, so you hire a freelancer to lug things around. But then you get to the part where you want to run electricity outside, which terrifies you, so you hire a contractor who specializes in electrical. After the deck collapses because you didn't anchor the support posts deep enough, you hire a design studio to do the whole thing over from scratch—including researching how deep the support posts should be.

We'll learn how to evaluate these different types of designers later in the book. Before you hire *any* of these people, let's make sure your place of business is ready to accept them. Can't plant seeds until you prepare your field.

GETTING YOUR HOUSE IN ORDER

Before you hire a designer, set up the situation this person needs to be effective. Bringing any employee into an unprepared environment where they don't have the tools or authority to succeed is unfair to them *and* a huge waste of your hard-earned money. It also burdens the other employees who aren't sure what to do with this new person.

A few years ago, I made plans with a friend for breakfast. She was late. When she finally got there, she apologized, saying she'd been cleaning up for the housecleaner.

"Why in the world would you clean up for a housecleaner?!?" I asked.

"So she can actually clean, you idiot."

This made no sense to me, but I let it go. Otherwise, we would've argued about it for hours. About a year later, I got busy enough with work that my house looked like it could star in an episode of *Hoarders,* so I hired a cleaner. After a few visits, I found myself cleaning up piles and random junk so that she could get to the stuff I actually wanted her to get to.

I called my friend and said, "I get why you had to clean up for the cleaner now."

"I told you you were an idiot."

(My friends are great.)

The moral of this story is you can't drop a designer into your environment and expect them to succeed. You've got to clearly lay out your expectations, but you also have to set the stage so your designers come in and get to the stuff you need them to do.

Introducing a new discipline to your workplace

Let's assume you don't have a designer on staff. People have been going about their business and getting their work done, and now you're introducing a designer. Even if your employees have been *begging* you to hire a designer, this creates a challenge. People are creatures of habit and comfort. As difficult as they claimed their jobs were without a designer, having one *still* means giving up control of things. This isn't easy. All the complaining about having to do someone else's job is about to turn into complaining about giving their work to someone else. People are awesome.

A designer will absolutely change what your company produces, and they'll also affect how your company operates. You'll need to adjust your workflows for this new person, as well as being open to having them adjust your workflow once they arrive.

Before you throw someone into the mix, sit the company down and explain why you're hiring a designer, how the company benefits, and what the designer's role and responsibilities are. Explain how adding this skill set to your group makes everyone's job easier. (Including possibly going home earlier!) Thank them for going without a designer for so long. Talk to them about things that they no longer need to undertake *because* of the new designer. Tell them to expect some bumps as the designer gets integrated into the fold.

Then back your designer up when those bumps occur.

Your designer can't do shit without support from the person up top. If their job is to go in and change the way people work, the way the product behaves, and the way people interact with each other (all of which design *will* do), that's gonna ruffle a few feathers. When a colleague runs into your office and says, "The designer is changing things!" a well-placed "That's exactly what I'm paying the designer to do" sets the perfect tone. Remember, designers aren't out there doing it for their own well-being. They're your representative.

As tough as introducing a designer may be, it's infinitely easier than introducing a designer into a workplace where a bad designer has been nesting. We're talking industrial-sized smudge sticks. I once took a job where coworkers would walk to my desk and ask me to whip up signs for their yard sales. When I informed them that wasn't my job, they replied that the previous designer always did that stuff. I reminded them that the previous designer got fired for not meeting his deadlines. Eventually, they stopped asking. Had I been more willing to bend to their requests, we would've forever established that designers are the people who make yard sale signs for coworkers.

Clear the table of any shenanigans like that before your new designer starts. Delivering this message is much easier coming from you. Don't pass it off to the new person.

Understanding what designers are responsible for

This may sound obvious: a designer is responsible for design, right? By *design,* I'm talking about not *just* how something looks, but also how it manifests the solution to the problem it solves. Remember that nice young designer who worked at a big company—the one who wasn't invited to strategy meetings? By the time work got to him, the decisions were set down to the smallest details and all he did was execute. He wasn't designing. He was executing on someone else's design.

In truth, he needed to assert himself. But this chapter is about you. Design is the solution to a problem, something you pay a professional to handle. A designer is, by definition, uniquely qualified to solve those problems; they're trained to come up with solutions you may not even see. Your designer should champ at the bit to be involved in strategic discussions.

Make sure to use your designer's skill set completely. Make sure they're involved in strategy discussions. Make sure they're involved in solving the problem and not executing a solution that's handed to them. Most of all, make sure they see this as part of their job. If they don't, your design will only ever be as good as what people who *aren't* designers think up.

Giving designers the authority and space they need

Just as it's absolutely clear what authority your office manager, accountant, and engineers carry, make sure your company understands what authority your designer has. Let's go ahead and extend the definition of authority to "things they own." In the same way the bookkeeper owns the books and the engineer owns the code. (Yes, I get that technically *you* own it all. Work with me here.)

Trust your designers. Give them the authority to make decisions they're singularly qualified to make. Before you bring a designer into the company, decide what authority they have over parts of your workflow or product. Do they have the last call on user-interface decisions? Do they need to get input from other stakeholders? (Always a good idea.) Do they need *approval* from every stakeholder? (Always a political shit show. Trust me.)

The right answer depends on the type of organization you run and the skill level of the designer. But whatever that call is, empower your designer with the maximum amount of agency to do their job well. No one tells the accountant how to do their job, but I've been in a hundred workplaces where people told the designer how to do theirs.

A designer with backbone and experience won't have any problem carving out the room they need to work, but they can't do so if you don't grant them the authority. Otherwise, you run the risk of bringing someone in to follow the whims of those around them. That's not a full member of the team. That's a glorified Xerox machine, an asset used by the rest of the company whenever they need some pixels pushed around.

That's how someone who's supposed to work on your website's UI ends up making Lost Cat flyers for Betty in HR.

Equipping designers with the tools they need

This should go without saying, except I once spent the first two weeks at a job spinning through a draconian requisition process to get copies of Photoshop and BBEdit, which the company considered nonessential software. Someone from IT gave me a one-hour demo on how I could harness PowerPoint to do anything I needed Photoshop for. (I know I should've stopped him, but at some point my annoyance faded in favor of fascination at how much he'd thought this out.)

Like any craftsperson, your designer is only as good as their tools. Make sure they have what they need. Yes, it's fair to ask them to justify their use. No, you don't need to understand what everything does. Trust that *they* do.

Measuring success

How well you prepare your team for a designer, how well your designer gets along with everyone, and how professionally they behave means exactly jack squat if your designer doesn't succeed in their goals. Before bringing *any* employee on board, you should know how you'll measure their success. Will it be hard metrics? Do you expect sales or conversions on the website to increase a certain number? Is the goal to deliver a big upcoming project on time and under budget?

Your business needs vary, so I can't give you a magical equation for design success. But I can say: whatever your success metric is, make sure your designer both knows about it and has the authority to accomplish it.

I *do* have a story for you though. I took a contract-to-hire job once, and the creative director sat me down on my first day and told me that he wasn't sure what to expect of me and how I'd fit in with the rest of the studio. (Someone didn't get their house in order.) At the end of the contract period, he'd evaluate whether to keep me around. I was young and stupid, so I didn't press much and decided to blend in as much as possible (rookie mistake). When my contract was up, the creative director called me into his office and said I hadn't performed the way they'd expected. Which was odd, because neither of us really understood what had been expected. I felt shitty, wondering what I could've done better. And honestly, I'm sure the creative director felt shitty too, because he realized he hadn't properly set expectations for success.

So yeah. Don't do that. It should never be a surprise to *anyone* working for you that they're doing badly. Or doing well for that matter. Let them know what they need to do to succeed. Let them know they're succeeding. If they're not succeeding, help them adjust course. And finally, let them know once they've succeeded.

Writing the job description

The most important thing about readying for a designer is figuring out how your company or organization benefits from their involvement. What will you be able to do once they're here? Picture yourselves a year in the future. What do you hope to accomplish? Write those things down. They're the basis for the job description you're about to write.

Make a list of what you need this person to do. Not the technical skills they should have, but the needs you hope those skills will fulfill. Do you need branding? Interface design? Illustrations? Forms? What kind of business are you in? Is it editorial? Are you a retailer that needs a catalog designed? Don't forget to take care of your mobile needs. Trust me, you have mobile needs. (Trust me, you've had them since yesterday.)

The result of this exercise may look something like this: "We need a designer with mobile experience that can do branding and interface design for complex data." The longer that list gets, the more you'll pay for a designer, and this exercise may help you realize that you need more than one person. A capable illustrator who can build a responsive site and understands agile workflow is a rare unicorn indeed.

Now let's go find us some designers!

HOW TO FIND DESIGNERS

Where exactly do these people hang out? How do you find them? Like most things, the best way is to ask around. Someone you know has worked with a designer or a design studio before. If you're lucky, they're someone you trust, and the designers did good work. Alas, you may find yourself having to write an RFP (request for proposal), which is a life-shortening process not unlike covering yourself in peanut butter and running through a field of hungry bears. Don't do it unless you have to.

A few caveats: you may have to adjust your criteria depending on whether you're hiring for a studio or an individual designer. With studios, you're likely bringing them on for a specific project, so focus on how well-suited that studio is for that task. It's also easier to gauge their reputation. With a full-time employee, you need to consider whether they can handle all the projects you have—not only now but in the future. That's a taller order.

Referrals

The best way to find the right designer or studio is to get references from colleagues you trust. Find out who they worked with, how the project went, and how long ago that work was done. (The people they enjoyed working with may have moved on.) The majority of our clients find us this way. As an added benefit, your colleague (probably) won't recommend someone they know you wouldn't get along with.

Half-blind referrals

Barring a trusted referral, take a look at the sites you admire. Find out who designed them. Contact someone at the company and say, "Hey, I love your site. Who did it?" People love hearing that. They'll be happy to make an introduction. This is a half-blind referral. You know you like the studio's work, but you have no idea whether you're a good match. So collect a few names to reach out to.

Whatever you do, don't Google *design studio*. You'll spend a ridiculous amount of time sifting through the results with absolutely no context. It'll be like that time you opened up the hallway closet and raccoons jumped out, followed by everything you tossed in there over the last ten years.

Oh Christ. Not an RFP.

I know some of you work in places that require you to write RFPs or even their precursors, RFIs (requests for information).

I'll get to you in a second. Right now, I want to talk to the people that don't.

If you're not under some weird obligation to write an RFP, don't. The single most important data point in choosing who to work with is whether you work well together. You need mutual respect and rapport. You need to find out whether you can spend three months to a year in a room with these people and not want to destroy each other. RFPs get in the way of establishing that relationship. You're gonna get bogged down answering questions about the RFP's rules, instead of solving your design problem.

For those of you who have to write RFPs (hello, government agencies and universities!), keep it simple. Your RFP should state what the problem is, constraints to keep in mind (like time and budget), and the project's goals. Avoid any prescriptive solutions. You want to work those out with your design partner. Avoid labyrinthian rules that make reasonable people steer clear of responding. Don't make responding to the RFP a chore.

You don't want to pick a design partner because they scored high on your questionnaire, remembered to send the specified number of copies, and punched everything on your itemized, prescriptive list. You want to pick the design firm that does good work. That may be the firm that questions whether your list will achieve your goals.

Follow the same rules to figure out who to send the RFP to. Find the studios you want to work with. Call them. Let them know you're sending an RFP and make yourself available to talk.

Remember, you're not looking for a vendor. You're looking for a partner. A vendor fills your soda machine every Tuesday. A partner works with you to solve a problem. That's a relationship.

Once you've gathered a list of studios, it's time to evaluate portfolios. You may want to mix yourself a drink first.

HOW TO EVALUATE A PORTFOLIO

Every web designer or design studio should have an online portfolio.

Let's be clear: the website you want is *not* already in their portfolio. A common mistake clients make (except you of course) is to look through portfolios as if they can pick something off the rack and throw their logo on top. Think of it as visiting a tailor. You want to examine the quality of their work. You want to see if they work with fabrics you'd wear. You want to get an idea for the different types of suits they're capable of making. You are making a decision about whether you're going to let them take your measurements, but your suit hasn't been made yet.

Your job is to decide if you want to get to know the designers better. You're not making a hiring decision yet, no matter how impressed you may be with their work. You're going to spend significant time with this designer or studio, not to mention putting your business's future in their hands. Use the portfolio as a data point, not the deciding factor.

As you go through, look for the kinds of problems they've solved. Think in terms of complexity, range of work, and scale of client. Feel free to use your gut. If someone seems like someone you'd want to work with, bring them in and find out.

Is their work good?

Who cares? I mean, of course we care, but good is so subjective, and this is a short book. Hopefully, every designer thinks their work is good. You either agree or disagree, at which point all they can do is try to talk you into it. In the end, no one's learned anything. So let's sidestep the whole idea of whether the work is good and discuss whether the work is effective. Effective is something we can agree on. And measure.

Everything in their portfolio should be based on achieving a goal. Ask what each client wanted to achieve. Did they achieve it? For example, if my client hires me to increase website registrations by 25%, and post-redesign registrations go up 25%, I know the work is a success. A designer needs to speak to these things. They need to know each project's goal, explain their rationale to accomplish it, nail the solution's implementation, and then gather data to see if that solution worked. Every project in their portfolio should have a similar story behind it. Hearing those stories is how you find out if you're interviewing a good, goal-driven designer.

Think in the abstract

For some reason, San Francisco, where I live, has an inordinate number of crepe restaurants. They all feature the same chalkboard menu. It's a nicely drawn menu, mind you. The lettering is well done, the drawings are attractive. I know that if I enter a crepe place, I'll see this exact menu. I can't for the life of me remember which restaurant I actually like, because they all have the same damn chalkboard menu. The first crepe restaurant that presents me with a different menu will be the one I remember.

So if you're in the online sprocket business, don't look for the designer who does sprocket websites. Look for the designer who can apply what they've learned in other fields to yours. Just because someone hasn't done work in your industry doesn't mean they're not capable; they may approach it with a fresh perspective.

Consider this: Steven Spielberg made an awesome movie about a shark, but if he'd gotten stuck making nothing but shark movies afterward, *Schindler's List* would've been a *very* different film.

Look for people who've excelled at solving challenging problems in other fields, and see if they're up for solving your specific problem. This is a wonderful thing to find out during an interview.

Red flags in the portfolio

Red flags aren't necessarily deal-breakers, but you should explore them further when you're talking with a potential designer face to face. Make sure they can address your concerns.

All of the work is for the same client

Watch out for the design studio whose work is tied to one big client. Two scenarios: that client comes calling, at which point you move to the back of the line, or that client *stops* calling, in which case your work may not be enough to keep them going.

And watch out for the individual designer whose career has revolved around one client; they've learned how to work in one particular way. Find out if they're flexible enough to learn a new way of doing things without losing their confidence.

I once worked with a designer who loved to ski. All of her work looked like it was for a ski resort. It was kind of remarkable. She could make a soup kitchen look like a ski resort. In fact, she did. A designer needs to extend their expertise to the client's brand and industry. The design profession isn't about self-expression; it's about business and user needs. Your designer needs to adapt their work to fit the needs on the table. But if you run a ski resort, gimme a call. I have your designer.

A lot of the work is personal projects

This speaks to someone who is inexperienced, doesn't feel their client work is as strong as the work they do for themselves, or doesn't want to do client work at all. Lack of experience isn't necessarily a deal-breaker *if* you have a more experienced designer on staff who serves as a mentor. If your potential designer's been in the field for a while and they don't have a lot of client work in their portfolio, you could be looking at a communication or confidence problem. And if they don't really want to do client work? Well, you wanna roll the dice on that one?

A lot of student work

There's absolutely nothing wrong with giving someone their first job. But realize that's what you're doing, and don't expect an inexperienced designer to handle complex client relationships. (As their first client relationship, you'll certainly count as complex.)

Student work can also mean work for a lot of made-up companies. Which means a lot of made-up client interactions. I don't know about you, but I win every argument I have in my own head. Imaginary clients are great as a showcase when a designer's starting out. They're good practice. But they should disappear from a designer's portfolio very quickly after the designer gets real work.

A lot of "How I would've done this"

I've saved the most dangerous for last. No matter how good a designer is, they won't be able to persuade their client to do the right thing every time. But a designer needs to make their case, explain their reasoning, push for the right solution, and know when and if they're willing to compromise. (As long as compromising doesn't put the project's goal in jeopardy. More on this later. Keep reading.) When a portfolio contains examples of how a designer would've done something differently had they convinced the client, they're telling you a couple of things: they lack persuasive communication skills, and they're not good at getting over their losses. Don't become an example on their list.

Also, watch for designers who publish their versions of recently redesigned sites they didn't work on. Such as "Here's my reimagining of Craigslist!" They didn't go through a client process or work through use cases. They weren't aware of any internal considerations. Their version isn't design, because it didn't emerge from working with a client. It isn't a solution to anything. (Also, *reimagining* is a hateful word.)

Positive signs in a portfolio

Again, this isn't a checklist for hiring, but guidelines to help you bring in a strong designer to interview. A portfolio can have all of these things and the designer may still be wrong for you. Doesn't mean you read the portfolio wrong. Just means they were good enough to get to that step and no further. You'll probably interview many people before you find the right person. (Please don't hire anyone until you've spoken with a few.)

An eclectic mix of clients and industries

You want to hire someone who's solved different types of problems in various industries and who doesn't fear the unknown. This speaks to curiosity, a willingness to get out of their comfort zone, and enough confidence to understand that with a bit of research, their skills apply across fields. These are good things.

Solid storytelling

A good designer is a storyteller. They understand how to get you intrigued, when to reveal parts of the plot, and when to deliver exposition. Their portfolio should guide you through their site and spark your curiosity; this is how you want your own sites to work.

More important, the samples should have context. You know the adage that good work speaks for itself? It's bullshit. To properly evaluate whether this person is the right designer for you, you need to know the context for their work. What problem did they solve? What was their timeline? Which audiences did they address?

Their work makes sense

When you look at their examples, is it clear what those sites or apps are and what you're supposed to do with them? Does a shopping site invite you to actually buy stuff? Can you quickly tell how to book a flight on their airline site? That sort of thing.

A strong use of typography

When I go to a Mexican restaurant for the first time, I always get the enchiladas. If they can't make enchiladas, they can't make anything else. It's a cornerstone of Mexican cooking. When I evaluate a designer's portfolio, I first look at how they use typography.

Very simply: can you read the damn site? Is it scannable? Do you know what to read first? Is reading pleasant? Type is a cornerstone of good design, and type exists to be read. If a designer doesn't have a solid typographic grasp, I wonder about other holes in their foundation.

You want to visit the sites and use the apps

A web designer's job is to make sites and apps that people want to use! Are you looking at anything you'd use? If you find yourself visiting a designer's sites after reviewing their portfolio, it's probably a good idea to bring them in for an interview.

FIRST CONTACT

Once you've made a list of possible candidates, it's time to contact them.

Reach out to a few recommended designers or studios. Remember, the more people you contact, the more you have to manage. Pick a number you can handle. If none of them work out, start over. The initial contact can be fairly casual. Tell them who you are, give a brief summary of the problem you're trying to solve, and ask them to call you back. Boom.

Evaluate them based on response time, whether they ask the right questions, rapport, and problem-solving mindset. That initial call, casual as it is, can be the beginning of establishing a solid relationship that eventually leads to finding the people to solve your problem.

Even if they turn out not to be the right people for this job, they may recommend someone who's a better fit. Which means you can approach *that* person or studio with a solid referral from someone who understands the problem you're trying to solve.

Do me a favor though. After you've reached out to someone and you've spent time together going over your project, it may turn out that they're not the people you want to work with. Tell them. Be clear and upfront, and tell them why. A good designer is always looking for ways to improve, so finding out why they lost a job is great information. Honestly, there's nothing worse than a potential client who disappears on you. I guarantee you that you're not the first client that chose not to work with them. They know how to handle that call. You also find out a lot about someone's character when you're telling them they didn't get a job. Note those that took it in a professional manner. You may need design services again.

WHAT TO PAY FOR DESIGN

If a designer gave you this book and bookmarked this page, don't hire them. They've handed you the book to convince you of something they should be able to do by themselves. If they can't convince you of something so core to their own interests, how will they convince you of the harder decisions coming down the road? And if they've marked this page anyway after this intro, you need to consider how carefully they read things. So now I've done you *two* favors.

No need to thank me, we've got plenty of other things to cover. They have less to do with *what* to pay people and more with *why* you're going to pay them. We'll also learn when you should spend money and when not to. In other words, we're going to talk about value. Stick with me, I'll make it fun and throw a joke in.

But first let's dispel the stupid myth of design as investment.

Design makes you money

For years, people thought of design as something nice to have, but not yet crucial to what they did on the web. They didn't view design as the underlying system of a product or process that started at the product's conception. They saw design as a luxury. Like investing in art or *Star Wars* figures that you never took out of the packaging. Like if you held onto it long enough, design would *appreciate.*

Designers, in turn, tripped over themselves to write essays on design's ROI (return on investment). These were dark times.

We were selling design as a cost of doing business. A sunk cost. A necessary evil. I'm here to tell you a better story: design is a profit center. You'll make more money from your website than the designer ever will.

If you have a product that fills a need or creates a desire, and you take care to design it well, you'll do better than someone who has a similar product that isn't designed well. If you disagree, feel free to toss your brown Zune across the room in anger.

Design's value is most apparent when somebody disrupts a commodity market. Let's take the lowly thermostat. For years, a thermostat was a thermostat was a thermostat. They were ubiquitous white or beige things that you screwed to your wall and never thought twice about. The thermostat in my house looks

FIG 2: The Nest Thermostat, proof that good design makes people go apeshit about even the most mundane objects (http://bkaprt.com/ymfc/5/). Photograph courtesy Nest Thermostat.

exactly like the thermostat in my parents' house thirty years ago. If your thermostat kicked it, you'd stroll down to the hardware store and ask for a new one. You wouldn't much care what kind. And you'd probably choose based on whatever was on sale.

Then the people at Nest decided to take this lowly object and see if they could design a better thermostat. They did. To the point where I go to friends' houses and the first thing they point out is their Nest Thermostat (**FIG 2**). Let me repeat that: their biggest point of pride is their goddamned thermostat. So now you get either a Nest Thermostat or one of those other kinds. Nest applied design in a considered manner and got people excited about the most boring item on earth. Their design sets them apart from competitors so much that people pick their thermostat because of it—and happily pay more for the privilege.

Don't pay for what you don't need

In Mule's early days, we worked with a ton of startups. In theory, I love the idea of startups. (If you're running a startup and reading this book, I like you even more.) Here we have people with an idea, one that they've probably percolated in their heads for years. They've secretly worked away at it in their off-hours. They've imagined every part. They believe in their idea so fiercely that they quit their jobs to turn it into a reality. I can't think of a more noble enterprise. And that noble enterprise is why we don't work with them anymore.

As a design studio, we're a great place for problem solving. Research. Strategy. User experience design. We found that the biggest problem with startups—and this may apply to you—was they just wanted us to bring the thing that was fully formed in their heads into existence. What they wanted most was someone to extract and design that thing to their specifications. Which I totally understand. They weren't ready to have their dream questioned, researched, tested, etc. They didn't want someone else's version of the thing in their head. If your idea has legs, it'll pass all those tests. But if you're not in the frame of mind to have that happen, don't waste your money on a design team that works that way.

If you insist on producing things per your specifications, go ahead and hire someone who's willing to follow your lead. That may be a production designer, or someone without a lot of experience (i.e., someone cheaper), but hiring someone who'll challenge you before you're willing to be challenged only wastes your money and aggravates both parties.

The bigger issue is why you'd be afraid to have your idea challenged. Any idea worth its salt survives a good tire kicking, and it only gets better if you expose its flaws when you still have the chance to fix them.

We've also dealt with enough entrepreneurs who show up at our door because their investors told them to go get some design. They don't want to be here and they don't understand the value design brings to their product. So they begrudgingly sit through another thing their investor mandates them to do. And it's a shitty time for them, and a shitty time for the people they hate-hired.

If a potential client doesn't see design's value, they shouldn't spend a single cent. A designer can't do good work without the client's full participation. The good news is that without all that design time, they'll probably get to market before their competitors, like the Rio did. The Rio? Oh right, that was the first MP3 player. Beat the iPod to market by three years. You may have one in the bottom of a box in your garage.

A fair exchange of value

If I had a dollar for every time someone said to me, "Must be fun getting to do stuff you like all day," I'd have a huge stack of bills. Maybe not enough to live off of, but a fairly big stack nonetheless. Because at the end of the day, design is how I make my living. Yes, some days are fun. Most days are busy. Every once in a while, there's a rough day. I wouldn't trade it for the world though, because I choose to do this. As do millions of other designers. And I feel very lucky that I get to earn my living doing something I enjoy.

Like many designers, I put in time to get the education, which cost money. I've also done my stints in the salt mines, starting with the crappy design job at a copy shop where I laid out résumés and designed logos in under twenty minutes. I eventually learned enough about my trade that I felt comfortable hanging my name on a shingle. I took on all kinds of work until I had enough of a reputation that I could choose what I wanted to do and who I wanted to work for. And I did all of that by making sure I provided a fair exchange of value for what I asked in return: money. I offer a service for money, as most designers do.

If you've ever worked with designers, you may have noticed that the vast majority are more than slightly uncomfortable talking about money. Between the two of us, I'll admit that for most of my career I was too. But then I discovered two important things: one, when I was afraid to charge my clients what the work was worth, I spent time I was supposed to dedicate to solving their problems worrying about paying my rent; two, when you charge people what the work is actually worth, they pay more attention to the project because they've invested more.

"Must be fun getting to do stuff you like all day" is another way to say, "I don't think you should charge me for doing what you enjoy." It's usually followed by some attempt to convince a designer that this job will raise their profile, or look good in their portfolio, or some other form of shenanigans that plays to a designer's underwhelming self-esteem. It may even work.

But here's where it won't work. That designer who signed on to the job at a lower rate, or possibly even for free, isn't doing their best work. They may try to. But in the back of their head, they're worried about paying bills, keeping the lights on, and finding another client to make up for lost revenue. This isn't like getting the guy fixing your sink to knock ten bucks off the price. This is undermining the livelihood of someone you're about to enter a long-term relationship with.

Of course, an honest estimate goes both ways. The only thing worse than trying to lowball a designer is trying to overcharge a client.

So when you discuss pricing with your designer (and it should be a discussion), make sure they can stand behind their quote. Have them walk you through it and explain why they're charging what they're charging. You should get an itemized breakdown for the project's major parts. Some designers and studios may even be willing to give you an hourly list of costs. Just remember that if the job includes figuring out your overall strategy, a line-by-line breakdown may be impossible, since neither of you knows exactly where those costs reside yet. Better to deal with flexible buckets of time that accommodate a project's shifting needs.

It's always good to get a couple of bids. If one designer's bid is higher than another's, feel free to let the high bidder know they're charging more than someone else. Ask them why they're worth more. If they can't tell you, it's a red flag. But when all is said and done, what you want is a fair exchange of value. Is their work valuable to your business goals? Is their quoted price fair for the value? The better a designer demonstrates an understanding of your problem and the capability to solve it, the more value they bring.

If you're hiring in-house designers, remember they come in many shapes and sizes and at many tiers. Unfortunately, nothing would date this book faster than offering you exact amounts, or even ranges, for what to pay them. Salaries vary dramatically based on geography, experience, market demand, company type, etc. So if you're after an equation, I've got a simple one: pay your designers as much as you pay your engineers. Pay your design director the same as your other directors. And pay the ones willing to disagree with you twice as much as the ones who aren't.

Things cost more when they matter more

...and this is right and good.

Why are some logos $99 and others $1 million (or, like the 2008 rebranding of British Petroleum, $211 million)? The million-dollar logo didn't take ten thousand times as long to make. Say it with me: it's about the value.

Brand identity is many orders of magnitude more valuable to IBM or Coca-Cola as it is to an obscure startup. The thinking around a well-known brand demands an equivalent level of care, consideration, and expertise.

If you're an established, successful organization, you pay more for design because the cost of fucking things up is much higher—and it's much, much harder to design a strong, innovative solution within a well-defined, even institutional, context.

Of course, a problem's complexity is the other significant aspect of project cost. That's a familiar calculation for most clients: designing more stuff equals more cost. More about this in a bit.

Why I need to know your budget

Budgets are often a sticking point with potential clients. Design is about finding solutions within a set of constraints. Your project budget is definitely a constraint. A big one.

Look, you can get a website for $500. You can also get a website for $70 million. The former is gonna have less stuff on it than the latter. (Neither will necessarily trump the other. I've seen kickass $500 websites. I've also seen million-dollar budgets go down in flames.) Knowing how much money you've committed to a project helps a designer tailor solutions to that price point.

A budget also helps a designer know if they can work with you. For example, if I have a fifty-person team that I need to keep employed and insured, I won't be able to do so taking on $500 projects. And if I'm a solo freelancer, I should probably stay away from million-dollar websites.

Let me tell you a story.

My father was the kind of man who dressed up to buy a new car. Partially because he was a good-looking guy who enjoyed flaunting it, but also because he was an immigrant who came from a culture where you wore a suit for important events. Buying a car was an important event. As an immigrant teenager, I was doing my best to assimilate. It was bad enough that my mother packed sardines in my lunch. Having my parents show up at school functions dressed to the nines, while other parents wore stylin' Jordache jeans and super-cool Ocean Pacific windbreakers, would send me into a panic as I dreaded the beat-down coming from the other kids the day after.

So we drove to the car dealership. The Fury, which had served us well, didn't have another Philadelphia winter inside it. For this particular occasion Dad decided on a sharkskin suit that shimmered from brown to olive, a dark yellow shirt, and a solid black tie. He accessorized with a Marlboro dangling from his lips. I came along, in an ill-fitting leisure suit my mother the seamstress made, to perform translation services. As immigrant children do.

At the lot, my father beelined to the brand-new, top-of-the-line Dodge St. Regis R-body with a straight-six engine and a whopping 12 miles per gallon in the city. It was ridiculously beyond our budget. The salesman wandering in our direction had no way of knowing this, of course. He saw a dapper man in a sharkskin suit who was ready to buy a car.

Twenty minutes later, we were test-driving the St. Regis through the Philadelphia suburbs. It handled delightfully for a boat on land. I sat in the back as the salesman described the various amenities and options available. I'd translate and add, "Dad, we can't afford this." To which he'd reply, "Shut up. Ask him if the seats are heated."

As we pulled back into the lot, the salesman's pitch got progressively stronger to the point where my father, now completely enamored with the car, finally had to admit that it was nowhere near our budget. And I was the one who had to deliver the message.

I'll never forget two things from the following interaction. The first was my father's look of embarrassment as he realized he needed to tell the salesman he couldn't afford the car, which, in my father's eyes was akin to failing as a provider. The second was the salesman's reply.

"Why didn't you tell me what you could afford?"

Buying design, like buying a car, is a financial transaction. Money comes up. In fact, budget is the first thing we ask prospective clients. This question tends to make people nervous. I've had clients flat out refuse to tell me, saying that if they disclose that information, I'll tell them that's what the work will cost.

That's partially true.

I'll tell you what you can get for that amount. Then we can talk about whether you need that much design. But most of all, that number tells me how to guide you toward the appropriate solution and avoid solutions outside of your price range.

Not everyone knows what their budget is. That's okay, we'll discuss a few options. Some below your price range, some above. But if you know what your budget is, let us know. It'll save us from having to look at everything on the lot.

My dad ended up going home with a Volaré station wagon. It made my mother very happy. Five years later, after it had run its course, he tossed me the keys.

Six months after that, I crashed it into a tree. I walked away without a bruise. It was a solid car.

Tell me your budget. It saves both of us time and money. And if you don't think you *have* a budget, someone's probably withholding it from you. I just blew your mind.

HOW DESIGNERS DETERMINE ESTIMATES

If you ask five designers for estimates on the same project, you'll get five prices that vary wildly. Which can be crazy-making. Let me explain how this happens.

A slew of data points go into putting a proposal together:

- **Scope.** The goals, size, and complexity of the project—the amount of work required to solve the problem.
- **Experience.** Experienced designers are more expensive. Designers who know how to handle convoluted problems cost more than designers who've solved easier problems. Complex problem solving is a skill that improves with practice. You benefit from all the mistakes they made in the past that they won't repeat with you.

- **Value, as described earlier.** The more influence the work has on your organization and the world at large, the more the work should cost.
- **Availability.** Supply and demand are factors.
- **Perceived awesomeness of the project.** Your project may be something the designer has been dying to work on or would like for their portfolio. Awesomeness is in the eye of the designer. Some clients try to abuse this by describing the work as a "great portfolio piece." Similarly, if the work is secret and the designer can't promote it in their portfolio, it'll probably cost more to compensate for the lost value.
- **The size and complexity of your organization.** These affect the resources for project management. Coordinating schedules and communication takes longer with twenty people than five. If it takes time, it takes money.
- **Timeline.** Amazingly, I've had a few clients think that needing something fast means we charge less since they're in and out quicker. Because FedEx also charges you less for delivery overnight when your package doesn't spend as much time on their trucks.
- **Costs of doing business.** Digital design and strategy don't require many materials, but skilled people and productive offices cost money, especially where you have competition for both. Rent and salaries are higher in places like San Francisco, New York, and London.
- **The asshole tax.** This is a thing. Everything else being equal, if you're a jerk during the business development process, designers assume you'll be a jerk during the project, and they'll charge you more to compensate for the pain in their ass. On the other hand, an angel discount often exists for nonprofits doing something admirable and previous clients with a good working relationship. If you try to skeeze your way to a discount, you will definitely be quoted a higher rate.

By far, the estimate's biggest component is the project's size and complexity, or scope. If we have an idea of the type of work you're after and know your budget, we can tailor the solution to meet that budget. The important thing about scope is that once it gets decided and signed off on by both parties, it doesn't increase. We're building what we're building.

But how can you know the level of effort something takes until you're more familiar with it? That's a great question. And that's why we call it an estimate. During the project's discovery phase, we get deep into the guts of things, and if we find that the project's more complex than you originally described, we discuss it together. We do a little horse trading within the scope: add some time here, deliver a little less there. If a project is complicated enough, some designers do an initial discovery engagement, including all of the project research, so they can put together a more detailed and refined proposal for the rest of the project. Yes, you pay for this.

So when you look at bids ranging all over the map, you're not comparing apples to apples. You're seeing an intricate model of supply and demand and timing. The company that sent you a bid for $100K may have bid $80K if you'd shown up a month earlier. And the company that bid $250K may have bid $175K for a similarly complex job if you were a nonprofit rather than a luxury resort company. Estimates aren't really a matter of whether you want to pay $50K or $100K, but whether you're willing to pay that particular amount for that designer at this time. Honestly, nothing is more important than picking the right people to work with as you're going to be spending a lot of time together. Choose who you want to work with first, and then decide whether you'll pay them what they ask.

GET A CONTRACT IN PLACE

All designers, big and small, should be working with a contract. A designer that works without one doesn't take their business seriously. If you ask a designer to work without a contract or refuse to sign theirs, don't be surprised if they turn you down.

No one expects a project to go wrong. But it can. Miscommunication. Strategy changes. Expected funding falling through. The freelance designer you're hiring could have a medical emergency. The studio you're hiring could get acquired by Facebook. These things happen. A well-written contract, one that protects both sides, ensures that if these things happen, contingencies are in place and everybody knows what to do. No surprises.

If you're in a large company, you probably have a standard contract for partners. Expect them to make changes. If your designer hands you their contract, I expect that you'll want to make changes too. You'll have to agree on which one to use.

I'll leave it up to the two of you how long you want this dance to go. Be aware that if you're working with a looming deadline, every day you spend debating contract minutiae moves your deadline back a day. Lawyers sometimes enjoy circling each other. Oh yeah, your designer probably has a lawyer too. And if I were you, I'd be concerned if they didn't.

The kill fee

Which brings us to a topic that's near and dear to me. Of all the clauses in our master services agreement, none has caused more grief than the kill fee. To sum it up: if you hire us for a project and your company wants out of the contract for reasons that have nothing to do with the quality of our work or service, you owe us a percentage of the remaining project budget. Here's why we're not going to let your lawyer strike it from our contract: if you've committed to do a project, we've reserved that time on our calendar for you. We've stopped looking for jobs to fill that timeframe as it's now yours, and we want to make sure you get our full attention. But if we're working on the project and doing a terrible job, you can flat out fire us. That's on us. (A whole chapter on firing designers is coming up in Chapter 6!) But if we're all moving along okay and your company unexpectedly eighty-sixes the project for reasons beyond our control, the kill fee kicks in. Because now we've got a hole in our schedule, and we need to protect ourselves against that. It's no different from when your doctor charges you for missing an appointment without twenty-four-hours notice. You're not giving them enough time to fill that appointment, and you're affecting their livelihood.

So if we're working on a contract together and your lawyer says, "I'm gonna strike the kill fee," do me a favor and tell them not to bother, because I'm not budging on that one. If you were in my shoes, you wouldn't either.

When to pay

Most studios, us included, insist on a deposit based on a percentage of the project before we start work. Depending on the project's size, it could range from 25% to 50% of the total project cost. Design studios aren't a high-margin business. Getting that money up front gives us the running room to get the project going and dedicate people to your job.

"Why should we pay someone for work they haven't done yet?" you ask. Excellent question. But let me remind you that you pay for flights when you reserve them, not when you get to your destination. You're paying to reserve a limited resource: our time. Unlike an airline, we won't ask you to pay for the entire flight when you reserve it, and if you come by our office, we'll give you the whole soda can.

If the project is big enough, you may have a couple of payments due at agreed-upon milestones, with a final payment on completion. I advise designers to define completion as something within their control. For example, if your designers are delivering front-end code for your internal team to implement, completion should be defined as the delivery of final code, and not implementation or launch. Because those things are beyond the designer's control. Should your implementation team be called away to put out a fire on another project, we can't in good conscience have the design team waiting for them to get back to work on the original project to get paid.

3 WORKING TOGETHER

BEFORE WE START: you may find this chapter hard to swallow, but it's also the most important. So remember that I love you. This is where I tell you the things you do wrong. Don't kick yourself; I've made these mistakes too. By the time you're done reading this, you'll be doing more things right than wrong, and have the envy of your peers.

Once you've hired a designer you need to trust them to do their job. This is harder than it sounds.

When we started Mule, I did all the visual design. As we grew and took on bigger projects, we eventually got more work than one designer could handle. We had to hire others. I had one rule: I wanted to hire people who saw and did things differently, who added another point of view in the room when we solved problems.

We got lucky and hired some good designers who fit the bill. They also had less experience than I did, which was fine. After all, I was the design director. It was on me to guide their designs and ensure the quality of the work leaving our shop. But those first designers we hired...I put those poor people through hell. (If they're reading, they're vigorously nodding along.)

The urge to grab their mouse and make decisions for them was incredible! I'm pretty sure I did so a couple of times. (Same designers now nodding more vigorously.) It got to the point where my cofounder, Erika, had to pull me aside and say, "Let the designers do their jobs!" It's excruciating to let people do their jobs if you think you can do it better. But I wouldn't have done it better. Only differently.

The real trouble was that I already had an idea of where I wanted their work to go. Despite my one hiring rule, I wanted my designers to make the same decisions I would, and I was frustrated I couldn't lead them to that exact solution. So I did it myself.

I was the one with the problem, not them.

My desire to take over other designers' work significantly affected the work and my business. First, I was destroying these designers' confidence and training them to look over their shoulders to see if I'd jump in on every project. Second, I was ensuring that my company could never grow beyond the amount of work one designer could do.

Why am I telling you this? I want you to see that I totally understand the urge to intervene and dictate how someone should do their job. More than that, I want to convince you why it doesn't achieve your goals.

Don't get me wrong, designers *need* clients to participate in the design process. You're critical. We need to do a better job of explaining your role in making the project a success. (It's coming up.) Because your position is one that uniquely suits you: the client. And you've hired a designer to fill the spot that uniquely suits them: the designer. If you're doing *their* job, who's doing yours?

RESIST THE URGE TO JUMP IN

I get it. You're excited. Maybe this project is your first one, or you've fought for years to get the budget to do this right. It's the culmination of endless meetings, conversations, and pitches on why it's crucial to your business; you're naturally enthusiastic that it's *finally* coming to fruition.

Or you're terrified! Holy shit, you handed all your money to these people, putting your livelihood in their hands, and they're probably going to cash the check, buy expensive shoes and eyewear, and take off for Hawaii, leaving you in your boss's office to explain what the hell happened.

Or your boss is breathing down your neck asking for constant updates. When can your boss see what the site will actually look like?!?! Your boss is an impatient person!

Relax. Trust yourself. Trust yourself because you're the person who hired them, and you did your homework. Their references checked out. They did good work for everyone else, and they'll do good work for you. I'm not asking you to trust *them*. I'm asking you to trust yourself. You hired well. Now let your designers do the thing they do, and let them do it the way they know how.

Nothing derails a design project, heck, *any* project, like a lack of trust. Once you've lost trust in someone, that shit is palpable. It's in the air. You want your designers focused on solving the problem, not managing your worries.

If you *do* have worries—get them out in the open as soon as possible. Ask the designer to put a plan in place that addresses your concerns. If you don't know what something means, ask. If you need something by a certain date, say so.

Don't stress about looking dumb in front of a designer. I guarantee they're worried about the same thing. The sooner someone says, "I don't know," the quicker that becomes an acceptable thing to say. Ninety percent of the world's problems come from someone afraid to admit they don't know something. Be honest about whether you have experience with the type of project you're working on. This applies to both clients and designers.

Does that mean we shouldn't hold anyone accountable? Heavens, no. You have a big role in the project's success. You should work on project timelines together with your design team and have regular check-ins. And your design team should update you on their progress. (More on this in a bit.)

RESPECT THE DESIGNER'S PROCESS

The designer's process is what made your designer successful enough that you decided to hire them. If that process worked for previous clients, it's highly likely it'll work for you too.

We once bid on a fantastic project, the type of work we enjoy and do well. Everything was lining up: the timeline was realistic with an ample budget, and the clients were smart and knowledgeable about their audience. A dream project. (Like yours.) So we talked to the client, got to know them, scoped out the work, and submitted an estimate. Then we waited.

The client called after a week. They'd gone through the estimates and narrowed it down to three design studios. They couldn't figure out which to choose, so they came up with a plan. They asked each studio to create a concept for the site and even offered to pay for the work. (In the industry, we call this a bake-off. It's a terrible practice.)

Except we said we couldn't do that. Not because we didn't want the project, because we very much did. But that wasn't our process. Our work relies on research as the first step of the design process. We gather user data to minimize the risk of failure and to optimize the chance of success. Until we've done so, we're guessing. We're throwing things against the wall to see if they stick. That isn't the path to good design.

Good design doesn't stem from intuition, talent, or luck (although I'll take a smidgen of each). It comes from research and understanding. We told the client this was a process that worked, one we stood by. We said the work in our portfolio— the work that made them approach us as potential partners— resulted from this process.

They politely listened, thanked us, and then hung up. I went back to looking for my next client, thinking that was the end of this one. And I was honestly amazed when they called back to offer us the job.

I'd love to tell you that our argument convinced them, but it hadn't. The other two studios, who agreed to do initial concepts without any research, did. Their concepts were nothing close to what that client needed. How could they have been? Beware a designer who tells you they can solve your problem without doing the legwork of research. That's not good design, it's a magic trick. They're either lying to you or themselves.

A DESIGNER ONLY HAS TO WIN A JOB ONCE

You did your due diligence in finding the right designer, and everything went well enough that you hired them. Now that you've awarded them the job, they've earned the right to succeed at it. Your job is to do everything you can to help. Their success is your success.

When I say a designer only has to win a job once, I mean a few things. You need to grant your designer the space they need to create good work. Give enough trust and freedom so they can try ideas that push boundaries without fear of losing their job. A designer who's in constant fear will solve problems in the safest, least challenging way possible. They feel they don't have the necessary support to innovate or try directions that may fail. In other words, they do boring work. Make sure your designer feels secure.

You also want to run interference from others, including other designers. As a consultant, I often work with companies that have in-house help. They hire me for various reasons: sometimes their designer is busy with another project. Or the designer doesn't have the skill set. Or, honestly, they plain don't trust the internal designer with a specific task. I was in that situation at the start of my career, so I'm sensitive to it. Whenever possible, I pull the internal designer into the project. After all, it's smart to have someone on the client team on board so what we learn during the project stays with the company.

But every once in a while, this internal designer feels slighted. Maybe they wanted the job for themselves. Maybe they felt they were capable of doing the work. (And perhaps they were.) So they make competing work and present it to the client lead. This sucks. For one, it muddies the water. Now we need to deal with rogue work and spend time, energy, and, of course, money dealing with the situation. For another, it undermines your authority. You awarded the project to someone else. If the internal designer is working on the side, they don't trust your decisions. A designer who wins a job shouldn't have to compete to keep it.

On the other hand, if a designer isn't working out or doing the job to your satisfaction, fire them. Chances are they're as unhappy with the work as you are.

I've had clients show up at our door and pitch their projects, only to say they'd awarded the project to someone else a few months before. But they weren't happy with them. So could we quietly work in parallel while they figured out how to deal with the other designer? Of course we said no. I won't take on someone else's project, and I won't work for a client who has trouble telling a designer they're not doing a good job. Because if *I'm* not doing a good job, I need you to tell me! I can't risk you hiring another designer behind my back.

BE HONEST ABOUT HOW INVOLVED YOU CAN BE

We begin every project with a kickoff meeting. We encourage the client to invite everyone who wants to attend. Sure, it makes things hard to organize and introduces a hurly-burly element, but everyone who wants to be heard gets to be heard. People who may not normally be involved in the project get a chance to speak their mind, which often includes crucial pieces of information.

But we can't effectively complete a project under any cost-efficient deadline if the client team consists of everyone in that meeting. You need to pare it down to a core group, a cross-disciplinary team that can devote a significant amount of time to finishing the project.

More important, we need you to be honest about how involved you can be. The design process requires client participation.

At minimum, you, or someone on your team, should expect to:

- Project manage your side of the project
- Coordinate your team
- Question and challenge recommendations based on your business goals
- Make decisions based on work in progress
- Provide feedback in one voice
- Provide all agreed-upon assets
- Meet your deadlines

Depending on the size of your organization, your other responsibilities, and the project's scope, you may not have the resources for a day-to-day role.

The number one reason projects get delayed is waiting for client feedback. Losing momentum sucks. Rather than risking project deadlines to make sure you're involved in every aspect, delegate the role to someone you trust. Your new lieutenant and the design team can work out key points in the project where your involvement is necessary. While you don't want to be a bottleneck, you also don't want to be surprised by the outcome. The trick is balancing your participation so the team gets the most from your input.

GIVE THE DESIGNER ENOUGH INFORMATION TO DO THEIR JOB

When a designer says they need to know something, take them at their word. I've been on projects where the client held on to some key detail about the company, because they felt it was too sensitive for the designer to know. That's like not telling your doctor you smoke. (You shouldn't smoke, but if you do, tell your doctor.)

If you have information important to company strategy, like moving from a subscription model to an ad-based one, or even tangentially related to the project, like a re-org that could affect workflow, let your designer know. Every piece of information you withhold increases the project's risk of failure.

A professional designer keeps their clients' information confidential, whether they've signed a nondisclosure agreement or not. What they know about company strategy influences how they approach the job.

DON'T DIVE-BOMB

Look, we like each other enough at this point that I can be straight up. You've got a design team and a bunch of internal folks working on a solution that benefits everyone, especially you. They're working toward that big goal you had a hand in creating, and you're checking in at key points, as we agreed earlier.

They've been busy preparing to present the work to you. They want to show you they're on the right path, and they want to take pride in their work. (You want them to be proud.) So they've probably spent time on a presentation that explains, alongside supporting data, why they've made the decisions they did.

Let them explain these things. You may want to jump in and give your instant opinion. You may have a quick reaction to something they're showing. Sit on your hands and let them finish telling you why they made the decisions they made.

The last thing you want is a team focused on whether you'll *like* something or afraid to try something they believe will work because you've expressed a distaste for orange, photos, or the word *potato.*

Do you want your team focused on making you happy or making the project successful? Because those can be two very different things. A team afraid to do their best work because you may be unhappy doesn't do you any favors. And you're not doing them any favors by putting them in that position.

Think of it this way: say you've made subjective demands—not based on research or data but your personal likes and dislikes—on your team through the entire project. The team was scared to piss you off, or, more honestly, to get fired, so they executed every one of your requests. Even the ones they knew would tank the project. Because you insisted. Six months down the road, the project tanks. Who's to blame? Between you and me, since we're in a safe space and all, I'll be honest. Blame the design team. Because a designer shouldn't execute anything they feel won't work even if it means getting fired. But you don't wanna put them in that spot, do you?

SUBJECTIVITY GOES BOTH WAYS

When I say you don't want your designers making decisions based on subjectivity, that's a two-way street. A designer needs to be able to explain why they made the decisions they made. So when I ask you to let the designer do their job, feel free to remind them that this is part of their job too: the responsibility of answering, "Why did you do that?"

You didn't hire a designer to make your buttons blue, headlines big, or slideshows look click-y. You hired them to meet a business goal. Trust that they know how to do this. Ask them questions when you're uncertain of their decisions, and call them to the carpet when they can't give you a justifiable answer.

THE MAJOR DECISIONS OF A DESIGN PROJECT (AND WHY THEY MATTER)

The question our clients ask most often is, "When do we see pictures?"

It's understandable. "Pictures" are the first real evidence of what your project looks like, and we're happy people are exuberant about getting to that stage. But please keep in mind the reason you're going to be excited about those pictures is the work beforehand to make sure those pictures are headed in the right direction.

So let's look deeper into the design process, with a giant caveat. Every designer claims their own process, and the process for designing websites somewhat differs from the process for designing, say, orange juice packaging (three people got that and one of them threw the book across the room). But whether you're working in an agile or a waterfall process (or smartly between the two), all processes break down to some version of:

- Find out what the problem is
- Come up with ideas to solve the problem
- Pick the best idea
- Build it
- Watch people use what you built
- Tweak it as necessary

This is all design

From the minute the project starts, whether it's the kickoff, interviews, or some other method your designers use, you're inside the design process. Some clients tend to think of research and strategy as obstacles to design. Again, that's understandable: you wanna see stuff. But much like building a house, you need to do some surveying to make sure the house is built right. Fight the tendency to rush your designer into the "design" phase— we're in it. Look around and soak it in. Feels good, right?

Kicking off

We start every project with a kickoff. This gives everybody the chance to meet one another and begin to build relationships. We're about to spend a lot of time together. I want to know who's going to be at my side and what they'll be good at. There may be some tough discussions in our future, and I need to start creating a reservoir of goodwill right away.

The meeting also allows us to go over the project's goals, and see if you agree among yourselves on what your goals are. Yes, we study your facial expressions and body language. So when you say your goal is to increase yadda yadda by 10% and we catch your Head of Marketing rolling her eyes, you better believe we're gonna follow up on that.

Who should be in the kickoff? To recap from earlier: everyone who's working on the project. Bring the core team plus everyone who touches the existing site or will touch the new site. Don't forget anyone who could hinder our progress. The people whose feelings may be hurt that you brought in outside designers are the ones who need to be there the most. We learn as much about you from the people who disagree with you as we do from those who don't, if not more. And, yes, we do need to learn about you. Because your site or app will only be as good as the people maintaining it every day. Yes, it's a bit like therapy sometimes.

As we find things out during the kickoff meeting, we jot down questions for further exploration. Interesting insights often come from the "quiet people" who rarely say anything, so invite them too.

Discovery: find out what the problem is

The kickoff meeting is the first part of the discovery phase. Designers have all sorts of names for this, but it's research.

Let's deal with this right now: you must do research. It doesn't have to be onerous. Erika Hall wrote a delightful book called *Just Enough Research* (also from A Book Apart) that explains how you can do research quickly, effectively, and painlessly. You should read it. (Full disclosure: Erika Hall is also, at least as of this writing, my wife.)

Research makes it possible to do the right thing. You know who didn't do research? The stupid little pigs that built their houses out of straw and sticks. They made a great stew. Build your house out of bricks.

Discovery is so important, we won't take a project at Mule if a client won't do it. Research isn't an optional phase of design; it's the keystone under which everything else rests. Unless we take time to properly survey the landscape and approach our work with a solid understanding of the problem, everything we do is costly guesswork.

If you already have a clear idea of what you want to do, great, we'll test those assumptions. Time we spend on research now saves you tenfold time down the line. Research isn't a time-sink; it's a profit center.

Your design team should ask you and your team questions: how you do your jobs, what your workflow's like, and how to improve it. (A good design team often comes in to redesign your website and ends up reorganizing your company.) It's in your best interest to give the design team access to the people they want to talk to. Remember, they work for you, and your secrets will remain their secrets.

Your design team should also reach out to people who currently use your product or service, if it already exists, as well as the types of people you're aspiring to reach. The goal is to see how people use the product, ideally in their natural environment, and how they accomplish common tasks within your site or service. Focus on their *needs*—you should never ask what they want or whether they like something. That's how Hollywood works. So no, we can't accelerate the process with a focus group. The only thing anyone's ever learned from a focus group is who the loudest person in the room is.

How much research do you need? It depends on your project's size and complexity. Do enough that you pick up common patterns. If you interview ten people and hear the same thing over and over, I'd say you're pretty solid.

At the end of discovery, the design team presents their findings. Everyone will nod and agree at some things, gasp at others, and argue about a few more. But you'll know a lot more about yourself and your product, and everyone will have a clearer idea about what kind of solutions to explore.

Strategy: come up with ideas to solve the problem

Now that you and your designers understand the problem, you can devise a plan of attack. As a benefit of the research you did, you also have something to check those plans against.

This is a great time to evaluate constraints you came across in discovery. Sometimes you'll find that what you thought for years was a constraint is an inefficiency in your workflow. Other constraints are very real. Let's say you want an image-heavy site, but you don't have a photographer or an image editor to maintain it. That's a major constraint. So we ask if you're willing to hire one. If you aren't, we say we can't design an image-heavy site. If you insist on seeing one anyway, we say no again, because we can't propose a design solution you can't sustain.

Do discuss solutions of varying complexities and how they'd affect your staffing, workflow, and budget. You can be a little aspirational before you have to get completely realistic.

Strategy covers everything that makes up your site and the overall structure, which we handle via two intertwined phases:

Content strategy

What do you have that people want? People visit your site for your content; your success hinges on how quickly they find it, how useful it is, and how enjoyable the experience is. Don't underestimate how important a clear content strategy is to that success.

Let me say it again: your content is the reason people visit your site and use your service. No one comes for the visual design. Plenty of people read interesting articles on shitty-looking sites. No one goes to pretty sites to read stuff they don't care about. (That said, if your customers have a choice between reading something they care about on a shitty-looking site and a pleasant-looking one, they'll opt for the second.) The visuals support the content, not the other way around. This is sometimes hard for designers to hear, but they need to be reminded every once in a while.

A strong strategy considers your audiences, content types, resources, and workflow. How do you create and maintain content? How do you define content categories? What is your editorial voice? Which tone suits different users and contexts? Strategy accounts for every possible way your user interacts with your content. Without it, you've got nothing, so start early. Erin Kissane wrote a fantastic resource called *The Elements of Content Strategy* (also by A Book Apart), which I wholeheartedly encourage you to read. (Finish this one first.)

Working through your content strategy will take time, dedicated people, and coffee. You and your design team should check in regularly about it.

And, no, you aren't looking at pictures yet.

Information design

Once you know what you have, figure out where it lives. We need to make sure people can find it. Designers will most likely show you what this looks like in diagrams with boxes and arrows, called *wireframes*. These come in many forms, from nice, clean diagrams to sketches on a whiteboard and interactive prototypes. The form doesn't matter. The results do. If your designers are fans of a more agile process, they may skip wireframes altogether and build interactive prototypes. For sites with a lot of content, this phase is called *information architecture.* For more application-driven sites, this is generally called *interaction design,* because it focuses on how people get from point A to point B. Airline sites have interaction design to show you how you should be able to book a ticket and then lots of content to explain why you can't.

Information design identifies the unique templates that make up your site. What's a template? Great question. For our purposes, a template is a page or screen type. For example, let's say you run a shopping site. Your most obvious templates are a product page, category page, search results page, and shopping cart. If you run a news site, you probably have an article page and a section index (Politics, Opinion, Sports, etc.)—you get the idea.

As we start to organize the site, our earlier research comes in handy. (It does that. I hope by now you're convinced.) We look over what users said during the discovery phase and organize information in a way that makes sense to *them.* The words they used to describe things? We want to use those words. The way they told us they make decisions about buying shoes online? We wanna take that into account and make sure the site is built around how *their* heads work, not how your company is organized. Your users don't care how your company is organized.

Visual concept: pick the best idea

Here's where things get messy, *Lord of the Flies* messy. For the most part, everyone manages to stay objective and logical during research and strategy, but then we enter the magical word of subjectivity, color, and wonder. It's like the entire team takes a hit from the Cheshire Cat's magic hookah.

You're looking at pictures. You are not, however, looking at pictures of your final website. Visual concept's purpose is to describe an idea that your product could turn into but hasn't yet. A good designer makes initial sketches loose enough that you grasp the concept without getting mired in the details or specific interface elements. This is normal. Rough concepts also keep your designers from burning hours on directions that may get tossed.

Here's how we're going to avoid getting messy. Got a guess? Yep, research. Your design team kept that research in mind as they came up with ideas, which means every concept you see is grounded in reality and supports your business and user needs. Even as your designers push the envelope on those findings, and trust me, every designer worth their salt tries to push that envelope, they're at least aware of *how far* they're pushing.

Your designer will gather your feedback, ask a few clarifying questions, and then return with another round of work. With every round, it should get closer and closer to the real thing. We'll talk about how to give useful feedback in the next chapter.

The goal of this phase is that you jump up in your chair and scream, "Yes! That's it right there. Make it like that!" Be prepared for that moment to take a few iterations, which are normal parts of the process. A designer who nails something right out of the gate isn't good—they're lucky. A designer who works with you, listens to your feedback, pays attention to your users' needs, and brings the work closer to the mark with each iteration is good. You don't want to rely on luck. You want someone with a proven process that ensures you success time and again.

Execution: build it

Now that you've chosen a concept, it's time to refine and turn it into a system for the templates we identified during information design.

Expanding the system to the most commonly used templates allows your designer to flesh out the concept into an honest-to-goodness design system that starts to resemble your final site or app.

Let me state for a minute that we have tons of ways to do this. Some people make templates in Photoshop. Some head directly into code. Most people go somewhere between the two extremes. There are also many techniques that rise and fall in popularity every day on how to do this work, but the purpose of this book isn't to endorse or criticize them.

Much as the best camera is the one you have on you, the best development technique is one that works for the people you hired. Ask your design team about their development philosophy and why they work the way they do. A good designer should be excited to answer that question, and their excitement should lead you to the confidence you need to let them do their work.

A good team doesn't ask how you want the project done. They tell you. They tell you why it works for them, and they're transparent about what they're doing.

Under no circumstances should you impose a method of working on a design team that they're not comfortable with. When it comes down to it, do you care that they're agile or that they're getting shit done? On time and on budget? That's the goal. Putting a new process in front of a team puts that goal in jeopardy.

Of course, if you're reading this as the leader of an internal design team, you certainly have a say in their methodology. But if you hire an outside team to do the job, you're hiring them *and* their process.

Testing

I put this at the bottom, because I had to pick a place. Testing can and should happen throughout your project, as your designers can test for different types of things.

You can test for language and usability with wireframes, whether interactive or simple paper prototypes. You can test if people can figure out where things are, and how they'd complete common tasks using nothing but black and white boxes.

Once you have some code, you can test whether the interactive elements make sense. Find out if people get from point A to point B.

Test the living daylights out of the product before you launch it to the public. It's also not a bad idea to beta test it with a controlled, small group before you release it to the world.

Testing deserves its own book. It's neither in the purview of this one, nor am I the author qualified to write it. But I would like to cover two aspects of testing.

First, do it early and often, like voting. You get more value out of small, informal tests done on the cheap than dumb, expensive ones in rooms with two-way mirrors—especially toward the project's end when the deadline looms, everyone is tired, and nerves fray.

I'll tell you a secret. I do most of my testing by grabbing people who're on the way to the bathroom. I say, "Hey, can you look at this real quick?" They're stressed out with a full bladder and don't have time to putz around, which means they need to make a fast decision. They're also less likely to be nice, because I'm keeping them from peeing.

Second, don't test for preference. Test whether something works. Test whether people can accomplish tasks. Test whether people can find things or whether the language you use to describe things matches the language *they* use. But testing whether people like A or B is the road to regret, damnation, and blown budgets. (A/B testing is a great way to get incremental improvements to the solution you've chosen, but a terrible way to choose that solution. Put another way: you can't A/B test your way to inventing Google. But you can A/B test your way to a better Google.)

We once worked on a project for a site with an active community. We showed our client a couple of concepts. And this is totally on us, but we neglected to tell him not to publicly post them. So he did. He posted the concepts to the site's community for feedback. Over two weeks of spirited feedback followed, where by *spirited,* I mean that users started arguing with each other. That devolved into name-calling. A few people even presented their own concepts, and one person wrote a 5,000-word post on how the site shouldn't change at all. Eventually, we had to start over. The concepts were so tainted that none of us could look at them without breaking into a cold sweat.

While you should have a strategy for informing your users about change, asking them to make choices along the way only muddies the water. *Simpsons* fans may remember the episode where Homer took part in a focus group and goaded everyone into designing The Homer: a double-domed, lime green, multi-horned Frankenstein's monster of a vehicle (http://bkaprt.com/ymfc/6/). (I'd love to include the image if I didn't mind being sued by Fox.)

That wraps up the phases your design team follows during a project. Does that mean you sit around waiting for them to finish and show you something? Nope. Read on.

YOUR ROLE IN THE DESIGN PROCESS

When I was a kid, my dad used to take me around to construction sites. (Shut up, we were poor.) We'd peek through holes in the wall to see what was going on inside. It was exciting! (Mostly because we didn't have cable.) Cement got poured, rebar was bent, molds were nailed together, fat guys in hard hats cursed each other out. But the most amazing part was watching this mystery of how a building got made unfold. You felt like you had a special preview of your neighborhood's coming attractions, like peeking inside presents before Christmas morning.

Many clients think the design process will be similar: peeking through the hole in the wall as their own building rises up. Unfortunately, many designers don't treat the process that way. They build a wall around what they're doing. Once in a while, they let the client get a controlled glimpse. Which is terrible. We need you inside the wall. You have some lifting to do. So put on a hard hat. If you're lucky, you may even get to operate the crane!

You're the subject matter expert

No matter how great your designer is, they won't ever be the expert in your business. You are. The designer is the expert in translating your message so other people understand it. They're the expert in translating your business goals into something people use. But they need your help.

Make sure your designer trusts your expertise as much as you trust theirs. Clearly delineate each of your responsibilities at the project's start. Make sure this understanding extends to the rest of your team too.

As a consultant who's called in to work with companies, I can't tell you how much better projects fare when everyone on the team knows their strengths and is eager to collaborate. If you have internal designers, I get them involved as much as possible. Because once the project's over, I'm going away. Either I leave the work in the hands of an internal design team who's intimately familiar with the thing we created, or I dump an alien piece of work on them and you watch the monkey scene from *2001: A Space Odyssey* unfold in your office. Pick the former. Trust me.

Hope isn't a design word

Clear, honest communication is the best way to keep a project healthy.

In the early days of my design studio, we were working with a fantastic client and had a great relationship with them. They were engaged, excited, and smart. But they had one fatal flaw: they were too nice. Let me tell you what I mean.

We have our clients sign off on each phase of a project. This reaffirms that we're going in the right direction and keeps things from unravelling beyond the last agreement. Once we get sign-off, we move on to the next phase. This also helps us finish projects on time. So, we're in the conceptual phase where we put out a few rough ideas, get feedback, and tighten the work—knocking ideas back and forth with the client until we get to the final design. When we agree it's solid, we move into code. That means the final design is something we come up with together.

These particular clients gave really positive feedback, which sounds great, except something wasn't right. The tone of their voices didn't match what they said. But hey, they were saying happy things, so full steam ahead. (Remember, we were still green to client relationships at the time.) We got to the final concept presentation, which theoretically was where they'd pick what their site was going to look like and give us their signature.

They did. We celebrated.

Except this time, as I sat with my team after the presentation, I told them something was off. These clients didn't look the way people do when they've finally seen their new website.

Someone on my team said, "But they signed off on it."

Technically, that was correct. They did. We could contractually head to the next phase. But my goal is to do right by my clients and have them leave the shop feeling like they're well taken care of. So I called.

"Are you guys happy with the concept you signed off on?"

Long silence.

"Not really."

"Yeah, I didn't think so. So why did you say yes?"

Their reply told me one of the most illuminating things I've learned in client services: "We didn't want to hurt your feelings, and we hoped you'd figure out that we weren't happy."

Hoping that I would figure out they weren't happy cost us four weeks of project time. Four weeks cost a significant amount of money.

Since that project, I now give a preamble before we enter the concept phase. It goes something like:

Some of the things you see will be right, some will be wrong. It's important you tell me which is which. You can't hurt my feelings—it's part of the job. Your negative feedback is more valuable than your positive feedback. If you don't speak up when something isn't working, I won't have a chance to fix it, which will cost us time and money we don't have. Let's promise to be totally, brutally honest with one another. Ready?

I tailor it a bit for each client, but you get the idea.

If a designer is heading down a path that doesn't work for you, please, please, please let them know. Designers are terrible at reading minds. Unless you tell them to stop doing something, they'll keep doing it. You can't hope someone into a course-correction.

You have my permission to hurt your designers' feelings. It's a good thing.

Also, I'm happy to report we got that client's project back on track and came to a design both of us were happier with. It lived in our portfolio for a very long time.

Invite argument

Beware a designer that doesn't piss you off every now and then. You hire designers to solve problems, not carry out your wishes. A designer's singular focus should be to solve the problem they've agreed to take on. If they agree to do something detrimental to that solution, they're not doing their job.

People ask why we named our company Mule Design. If you're ever lucky enough to find yourself at the Grand Canyon—and the government hasn't shut down again—ride a mule down to the bottom of the canyon. It's quite lovely. The first time someone tried riding down, they were on a horse. Horses, however beautiful, are also stupid. Sorry. The horses *jumped* right to the bottom. (Everyone loves this story by the way.) So they tried mules. The mules made it safely all the way down. They're sure-footed. They also have a reputation for being stubborn, but they're not. They just refuse to take any action that isn't in their best interest and, by extension, their rider's best interest. If they feel the path is dangerous, they won't do it. They resist and stop.

When you hire a designer, make sure they're sure-footed enough to veer away from any direction that doesn't serve your interests. Even if you ask them to. That means they may piss you off. But I'd rather work with a designer willing to have a difficult conversation than one who did anything I asked. Because in the end we're here to succeed.

When you ask your designer to do something and they ask why, they're doing their job. The ensuing conversation is invaluable in helping them solve the problem correctly. The two of you can probably come up with a better solution than either of you could have done individually.

Give everyone a clear role

One way to facilitate communication is to give everyone on your team a clear role in the project. Make those roles known to the design team. Let us talk directly to your developers about code and to your designers about design. Who on your team will be in charge of wrangling content? Who's the keeper of the brand? Hint: you shouldn't play any of these roles. We need you to have a birds-eye view. The design team may help you figure out who these people should be. At the project's beginning, go over tasks that need to be accomplished on your side; as we get to know your team, logical candidates to lead these tasks emerge.

Two important things here: you don't want to become the bottleneck for gathering information, and you don't want every single request shotgunned to your entire group. Both scenarios will slow things down to a costly crawl.

Help us keep the trains on time

Negotiate how much time you need to gather feedback from your team. Do yourselves a favor and add a day to whatever number you come up with. (No one in the history of design has ever delivered feedback early. I think it's physically impossible.)

Consider this one of the book's refrains: the most important deadline is your next one. Every time you or the designer miss a deadline in the middle of the project, it moves that final deadline back by the same number of days. Either something has to be cut to meet the original deadline, which of course means spending time debating what you'll cut, or the final deadline has to move. If you hired a designer from the outside, they may already have a project booked right after you. Remember, you've only hired them for a certain amount of time. If the project isn't done on time because of delays on your part, you may find yourself in a rough spot without a designer, or open yourself up to change orders or increased hourly rates.

Also, if someone on the project team, especially someone in a decision-making role, will be unavailable for an extended period of time, please let your design team know as you make the schedule. Out of the deadlines we've missed, 90% happened because a major stakeholder went on an unannounced vacation.

Avoid the swoop and poop

You're gonna have a bonanza of meetings, work sessions, and presentations. If you're interested in what's going on—and you *should* be since it's your money—do what you can to attend as many things as possible. Your design team will tell you which ones are *critical*. But do your team a favor and avoid popping into those meetings for a second to offer an off-the-cuff opinion out of context.

Since we're friends, I'll let you in on an industry secret. We call this the *swoop and poop*. I feel okay telling you this because you'd never do it. But when the whole team gets together and they've been debating for hours, arguing about research and data, and trying to come to an informed decision, nothing undermines the process like an exec bouncing through the door and saying, "I like the one in the middle!"

Don't be that person. Make sure you give your team a chance to explain where they are in the process. If they need your advice, they'll let you know. Understand the context before venturing your opinion.

Stick to your strategy

If you hire a designer to find a way to sell cheese online, and three-quarters of the way through the project you say, "We're not going to sell cheese anymore. We're going to be a video-sharing social network for dairy farmers. Can we stick to our original deadline?" the answer is no. The work that designer did, from the research on up, was geared toward a strategy that no longer exists. All of that work needs to happen again.

When you change your strategy, you reset the clock. The designer has no idea how far back to reset it until they've done the homework.

In some circles, this is known as "pivoting." From the Greek root *pivo,* which translates roughly to: "We are blowing whichever way the wind takes us today, and Poseidon help you if you got on this boat with a destination in mind."

In all seriousness, a change in strategy wreaks havoc on getting your project out the door in time. Which is why you need to discuss changes at length at the project's start. Make sure everyone is on board and it's as solid as possible. Course corrections during the process are natural and acceptable, but a change in destination means regrouping, replanning, restocking, *and* recharting your course.

Does this mean you should soldier on if it becomes evident that your strategy is flawed? Absolutely not. The cost of doing that is even worse than the cost of changing direction. But there's a cost either way.

No surprise guests on calls

I'll be honest. After ten-plus years selling design services for a living, surprise guests are one of the few things that still rattle me. I love working a room. I look into people's eyes and gauge how they receive the work. I read their body language and know when I may have to explain something. These cues fly right out the window when you present over the phone, which you have to do sometimes. You also have to contend with bad connections, echoes, and the dreaded, "We didn't hear you. Can you repeat it again?"

That pales, however, to hearing the voice of someone who was neither expected nor introduced at the beginning of the call. Same rules apply over the phone as in person: if you're in the room, I need to know you're in the room, and I need to know what your role is.

Someone who lurks in the background only to spring in with a surprise comment sows distrust. Transparency is a key component to working together.

Keep the design team honest

One of the most important roles you have in the design process is to keep the design team honest. Question their conclusions. Ask them to back up their work. "What led you down this path?"

is a fantastic question to ask every time they put something in front of you. Any designer who's doing their job should be able to answer that.

Set up regular check-ins. Beware of design teams who want to do a big reveal at the end and surprise you with a finished project. Don't let them hide behind a wall! The best work is done when both sides are checking in frequently, looking at work in progress, and validating conclusions on a regular basis. Believe it or not, this encourages innovation. A designer will be more willing to take a risk and try something new if they know they're tethered to a check-in and won't be allowed to go off course irrevocably.

Remain calm

Things are going well. Everyone is working hard and zooming toward the finish. You can taste it. But then something slips through the cracks. Maybe someone misses a deadline. That finish fades in the distance, and things seem insurmountable. No matter how well a project is going, there's going to be a slip-up *somewhere*. You may want to rip your designer's head off. That's normal. But keep calm. Designers understand how important this project is: how you fought for the budget, vouched for them to your bosses, and count on its success as a sign you've done your job. A good designer understands those things, and they should also be calm. After all, they do this every day—they've got it under control until they say they don't. (I'll tell you what to do then in Chapter 6. Don't skip ahead.)

Think of it this way: you're cutting a bagel in the morning. The knife slips and suddenly you're in the emergency room. It sucks. You're freaked out, which is totally understandable since you're bleeding. Which doctor are you gonna trust more? The one who freaks out along with you? Or the one who remains calm and acts like stitching on a thumb is a routine part of their job? That's what you want in a designer too.

And if you don't remain calm, that doctor may have to knock you out before they sew the thumb back on.

4 EVALUATING WORK AND GIVING FEEDBACK

I WAS LUCKY ENOUGH to be raised by a seamstress. Admittedly, this meant being marched off to school in a series of plum-colored, home-sewn leisure suits in the late '70s. But for all the shame and inorganic fabric I endured, I got to watch my mom work. The way a seamstress approaches her craft isn't too far off from a designer. They decide to take a client and discuss the client's goals, which in my mom's case was usually her specialty—wedding dresses.

Together, my mother and the bride would choose a pattern, feel out fabrics, and talk about modifications. As the dress moved from pattern to muslin mockup to the finished gown, the bride would come to the house to get fitted. Alterations were made, hems adjusted based on smiles and frowns. Both the seamstress and the client had important roles; without the bride's participation, my mother had no way of evaluating her work. Just because something fit didn't mean it was the right dress.

As a kid, I was getting a master lesson in client services. A lesson on how to treat clients and work *with* a client instead of *for* a client. I watched clients evaluate work. I watched them give feedback. And I saw how critical it was for both craftsperson and client to communicate and work together. (I also got roped into attending a lot of weddings.)

In this chapter, we'll talk about how to tell if the work is going in the right direction and how to communicate with your designer to keep it that way.

HOW TO EVALUATE THE WORK

"I don't know anything about design."

We already went over this. Who cares? The project's ultimate success doesn't ride on your users knowing anything about design, but how they respond. It rides on how well the design helps your users effectively, efficiently meet their goals in a way that benefits your business.

Your job is to be the business expert. Your knowledge of the organization and your skill set aren't things the designer can bring to the table. Your level of engagement in the design process and the quality of your evaluation of the designer's work determine the project's success.

Design is a series of checks and balances. The designer uses all of their intellect, knowledge, and skill to come up with solutions—and you need to come up with an equal amount of intellect, knowledge, and skill to evaluate and critique those solutions.

Challenging the designer's work in the most productive way possible is the essence of being a client.

As I mentioned in the last chapter, no one, and I mean absolutely no one, comes to your site for the design. (A thousand designers just threw this book across the room. Hope they weren't reading it on their iPads.) People come to your site to read articles, watch cat videos, see what their friends are up to, and scope out sales. They come because the site fulfills a need, whether it's a physical need (pants), an emotional need (cat slideshow), or a logistical need (airplane tickets). The design needs to support that content or function in ways that make its use clear, delightful, and memorable. The better design does those things, the more people will return to your site when they have that need or desire. When you evaluate design, think of the person having their need fulfilled. Can they do it? Can they do it in a manner they'll enjoy?

Subjectivity is weak

Let's do a quick recap on subjectivity for anyone skipping around. Because if I can drill *one* point home, it's this one. Your personal tastes are not a success metric. This is a business! We're going to evaluate the work based on whether it increases revenue, customer retention, or any other metrics we set up at the start. I don't care if you hate green. If the research points to green making you buckets of money, we're using it. I bet you'll like green then.

I don't want to single you out. Keep an eye on your designer's subjectivity too. Make sure they believe that whatever they put in front of you is the best way to solve the problem. They better back that up with solid research-based reasoning. You don't want them doing things because they "like" them either.

Nobody here gets to like anything.

Go back to the goals

You had goals when you began this project. (If not, go back to start. Do not pass go.) As the project progresses, it's easy to lose track of those goals. Especially when we sail the subjectivity-infested waters of visual design.

Is the designer showing you work that will meet those goals?

If you're telling the designer *how* to meet goals, you're dealing with a bad designer. If your designer doesn't understand your goals, you may be dealing with someone out of their depth. And if the designer shows no interest in goals, you're not dealing with a designer at all.

But say the designer *is* putting work in front of you and saying things like, "Our goal was to sell pants, so I made sure the product pages had nice photos of people wearing pants, an obvious way to buy those pants, and another way to get to different pants if these weren't the pants they wanted." That's good rationale. Your job is to evaluate whether those solutions help you sell pants.

You may know from your decades of working in the pants industry that pictures of people wearing pants creep people out. That's great feedback for the designer, and something only your experience can bring to the table. Don't assume your designers have learned all the tricks of your industry. Cut them a little slack. It's taken you a long time to learn what you have.

Where are you?

Fans of *The Wire* may remember that Major Bunny Colvin's training included always knowing "where you are." Right now, I'm at 209 9th Street on the third floor facing north. The idea is you can't truly evaluate your situation unless you know where you are. Try it. Where you at?

If the answer is "in the middle of a bookstore, trying to read a book for free," go to the cash register and pay up. Otherwise, carry on.

The same holds true on a project. You can't evaluate work unless you know where you are, because each project phase determines the kind of deliverable you get. Are you looking at a rough sketch to help set direction or a fully realized system? Are you supposed to pay attention to interface labels or are they placeholders? Do you care that the JavaScript isn't working? Etc.

Your designer needs to set the stage for you. Remember my speech about hope in the last chapter? (Go back and reread it if you don't.) Every design presentation should start with some form of: "Here's what we need your feedback on today." That may be followed by the helpful: "Here's what we're not ready to talk about yet." If your designer doesn't tell you these things up front, feel free to ask. Sometimes they need a little help. Otherwise, you may find yourself spending thirty minutes discussing JavaScript functionality that isn't slated to work for another three weeks.

Once we know where we are, reacquaint ourselves with the goals, and can look at the work objectively, we're ready to do some evaluating! But what exactly are we evaluating for? Excellent question. Here are general things to keep in mind.

Check your tone

This work will feature your name. It reflects how you present yourself to the world. Whether it's your main site or one product of many, it's going to be part of your brand, not the designer's. If you have an established brand, you probably have brand guidelines. Does this new work follow or expand on them in interesting ways? If you're establishing a new brand, does this work accurately convey who you are? Why didn't I call this section "brand"? I want you to consider every part of the work. Even—no, especially!—the tone in the copy.

You need to evaluate tone throughout the project's lifecycle. From the initial structure and color palette, to the navigation language later on, to decisions like whether you're the type of organization that puts everything in a slideshow (please don't be). You have to review details on how to treat bylines, manage comments, and handle offsite things like the way you speak on social media platforms. Which thing to focus on depends on where you are in the project. But you should continue to evaluate the tone after the project launches; periodic check-ins ensure your organization's tone is true.

Feasibility

When you're evaluating feasibility, consider two things:

1. Can you make it?
2. Can you run it?

We're driving toward a deadline. When a designer puts something in front of you, especially if it's technically tricky, evaluate the effect that piece of functionality has on your deadline. If you don't know whether something is technically tricky, ask. Here's a secret: they will always say no. But if it's tricky, they'll hesitate for a second before saying no. At which point, ask for an hourly estimate of how long it'll take to build it. Then double the number and ask if there's an easier way.

So you have the resources to build something. More important, can you run it? During the discovery phase, we find out how many people and how much of their time you can dedicate to maintaining the site. We call this the Oars Test. We're building a boat, and we need to know how many oars to include. Because the Queen Mary may be a lovely ship, but if it only has two crew members, it's not going anywhere. Yes, I know the Queen Mary doesn't have oars. Let's move on.

Remember who you're building it for

It's great you want to use your own product—I'd be worried if you didn't. But we need a lot more users for the product to be successful, and they're not all going to think like you. Remember, your goal is to achieve success (probably money) by helping people do something in a different and better way than they could before. Their goal is just to do that thing.

Along with research, a bit of empathy for your users goes a long way. No one will use your product because you think it's awesome. They'll use it because it makes their life easier or more fun. So if you're evaluating work and you find yourself saying, "This makes sense to *me*," you're in trouble. Instead, ask yourself if it would make sense to the people you're building it for. At some point, you and your designer should test the product with those people. Let *them* evaluate it. Make sure they can accomplish common tasks. Make sure the language on your labels makes sense to them. Remember that testing early and often is better than putting your testing eggs in one basket toward the project's end. You want to iterate throughout, not freak out when you're out of time.

Flow

You know what the worst smell in the world is? That's right. Hot cat food. I once woke up, ground coffee, scooped a cup of cat chow, put the coffee in the cat's bowl, and dumped the cat food in the coffeemaker. I'm not sure who was more surprised, me or the cat. It's important to do things in the right order. In this case, I should have made coffee and then fed the cat. It's also important not to do too many things at once.

When you evaluate a design's flow, ask yourself if things happen in the right order. Think of how people flow through the system. Does the design guide that flow? How do people enter? Are we sending them directly to what they need? Are we springing a pop-up ad on them three sentences into the article? (Please don't.) Do we let them enjoy the thing they asked for and then offer further places to go at the right time? Or are we pushing them through the front door while anxiously shoving a million other options that grab their attention?

The correct order seems obvious in some cases, like buying a movie ticket. You decide what movie you want to see, find out where it's playing, get a showtime, and buy a ticket. Unless you choose a movie based on what's playing at a certain theater, in which case, you swap the first two steps. The system needs to work both ways. The order isn't ever as obvious as you may think, because people are weird and wonderful and do things in all manner of ways.

A good design accounts for unknown knowns. The best systems don't need to change how users behave but bend to suit your users' needs. They're informed by how users *already* behave. Pave the cowpaths and all that.

Simplicity

Antoine de Saint-Exupéry said, "A designer knows he has achieved perfection, not when there is nothing left to add, but when there is nothing left to take away." You may know Antoine de Saint-Exupéry as the dude who wrote *The Little Prince*.

Simplicity is the key to success—and the hardest thing to pull off in design. When you do manage the feat, it looks like you've done nothing! Because, oh my god, it's so simple. Which is why the main ingredient of achieving simplicity is confidence. A good designer finds an elegant way to put everything you need on a page. A great designer convinces you that half that shit is unnecessary.

The more crap I remove from a website the more likely a user sees the thing the client needs them to. The clearer our path to the goal, the more likely we are to reach it.

If you take something away and the site still meets its goals, you don't need it. Burn it with fire. Let's define what we mean by "need": does it meet a major goal of the business or user? Is this the right place to meet that goal?

Internal real-estate battles are some of the biggest challenges to simplicity, especially in larger companies. One department gets upset that another was allotted more space, so they demand more space. Which is the tragedy of the commons. Let's say you have a common field where all the farmers bring their sheep. Your neighbor decides to bring ten more sheep than he did yesterday, which means less grass for your sheep. So you say screw that guy and get yourself *twenty* more sheep. Meanwhile Bud, the herder up the road, decides you both suck and gets himself fifty more sheep to graze. Now the sheep don't have enough grass, the field dies because it's overrun, the sheep die of malnutrition, and your town dies because there's no more mutton for stew.

This kind of internal territorial battle destroys your website (you realized I was talking about the website, right?). You're in a much better position to keep it from happening than your designer. Your designer can, and should, make a stand. But when push comes to shove, you're the one who needs to keep it from turning into a sheep show.

Hierarchy

Imagine you're going to a fancy party. A *really* fancy party. The kind where they announce you as you walk in. There's a greeting line. The most important person in the room is at the front, because, of course, she gets greeted first. Then the second most important and so on. This is hierarchy. (It's also a giant fun suck, which is why I avoid those parties. That's right, it's by choice.) But hierarchy has a point. Should you enter a party and introduce yourself to a duke before an archduke, things get out of whack. Treaties are broken. You end up starting a war. Thus, the receiving line was born.

We want people coming to your site to feel like a receiving line exists. Look at this first, then this. Now shake hands with the countess. You get what I mean. Things have an order, and we've thought them through. Feel free to replace nobility titles with user needs. (This is the most socialist line in the whole book, Mandy Brown.)

Hierarchy lets you know the important things are important, and the lesser important things are less important. (We got rid of everything that wasn't important, remember?)

When you evaluate the hierarchy of the site or app, where does your eye go first? Where does it go next? Are those places it needs to go? And how many of those places were ads? (I'm not against you making money, and I know those ads butter *both* our toasts, but when the first five places that draw your attention are ads, you have a problem.) Take the Bunny Colvin test: look at your screen. Do you know where you are? Do you know what you can do there? Do you understand how things relate to each other?

Going further, can you tell what the title of the page or screen is? Do the photos belong with the text? If there's an order to what you need to do or read, is that order obvious? As you flow down the page, do related items look related or seem like some random stuff to the side?

If you're looking at your homepage, can you tell what you should do within a second or two? Is that description as clear and concise as humanly possible? Has it been dressed up in corporate or hipster speak? Can someone who's not in your industry understand what it means?

As you evaluate, beware a tempting hierarchy fallacy: "Make it bigger!" Our reflexive response to not seeing something is to make it bigger. If you can't see text, make it bigger. If you can't see photos, make them bigger! Of course, now you can't see the ads. So we have to make them bigger. Which means we can't see the Buy button, so we have to make that bigger. This has made the logo almost invisible, so we make that bigger as well. Before you know it, you have the equivalent of a roomful of people shouting at you. And you can't hear any of them. All you want is to get the hell out of that room, because these crazy people are screaming so much. You want to go to a nice website where you can shake hands with a countess.

If you want people to notice something, make the things around it smaller. Your logo is big enough. Trust me on that one.

Now that you've evaluated the work, you need to communicate that feedback to the design team. I once had a client start their feedback with, "This makes me want to stab my eyeballs out." Let's find a better way, shall we?

HOW TO GIVE FEEDBACK

Let's assume the presentation went well. The design team put in a solid performance, cleaned up after themselves, and shook your hand with the appropriate amount of pressure on the way out. Hopefully, someone took notes and offered to make them available to you. Those will be helpful. You should've also agreed on when to deliver your feedback.

It takes designers years to learn how to guide clients on giving good, helpful feedback. In my experience, the first few (hundred) times I gave a client presentation, I was just happy to survive the ordeal. It didn't even occur to me that you may need help in evaluating the work. (It's fun to be young.)

An empathetic designer realizes that clients don't give design feedback for a living and don't really know what designers need at this point. Then they realize that it's part of the job to guide clients there. Because in the aftermath, you're alone with a stack of work that will affect the health of your organization, and your design team is returning to their office after a stop at the nearest Fluevog store.

So ask for feedback guidelines. "What kind of feedback do you need? What should I focus on and what should I ignore?"

Make sure you're clear on which elements you're supposed to evaluate. Are you looking at the overall brand, page structure, or typography? Did your designers use actual content, or did they take the easy way out and fill the comp with ersatz Latin and Flickr photos? (Guilty: I sometimes comp with Latin.)

If you're looking at code, is it production-level or prototype code? If it's the first, make sure to run it by the people in your office responsible for implementing it.

Build a shared vocabulary

A long time ago, I was working with this client. Good people. They were pleased with the research we did. They were pleased with the information architecture we did. But when we showed them the initial conceptual work, they weren't pleased. They said it wasn't *extreme* enough; they felt I was playing it safe.

Let me cut to the chase and tell you what the next thing out of my mouth *should* have been: "What do you mean by *extreme?*"

Unfortunately, I hadn't learned that lesson, as I found out when I presented the next round of concepts. My idea of extreme and *their* idea turned out to be two very, very different things.

Language is fun. It's also flexible. As one of our greatest philosophers, Inigo Montoya, said: "You keep using that word. I do not think it means what you think it means." Clients and designers have different vocabularies. They sometimes use the same words to mean totally different things.

Before you do any meaningful work together, you need to learn how to understand each other. All professions have their own idiosyncratic language. Design is no different. Even within various design fields, words take on a range of meanings. A template means different things to a user experience designer and a developer.

Personally, I feel it's the designer's responsibility to learn how to communicate with their client. They are, after all, communication professionals, and a good designer will have no problem asking you to clarify something you said. But as we know, people are less than perfect and often feel like asking a question makes them look stupid. (Au contraire!) It's in your best interest to learn a bit of their language too. Luckily, I've tacked on a handy glossary in the back. Enjoy. With some care, we can all learn how to use language to better achieve our mutual goals.

Explain this to me

Many designers believe good work sells itself. To be fair, they probably learned this at school. From people who are in school because they don't want to be selling design. But after these designers go through enough presentations where they unveil their work, say "Ta-da," and realize they've prepared nothing else as the client sits stone-faced and their palms get clammy with panic sweats, they'll learn that not even the best design sells itself.

Your designer should be able to give you a reason why they made the decisions they did. They should tie those decisions back to your goals. That's the logic you need to evaluate.

For example, "I've placed this ad so that it intersects the article body, thereby placing it within the reader's reading flow and increasing the ad's visibility and odds of the reader interacting with it." That's expert reasoning. It shows experience with reading models and business needs. "I put the ad here, because it fit." Not so much.

Your feedback should be based on how the designer's decisions reflect an understanding of your business plans. You may disagree with their decisions, but as long as both of you agree on the ultimate goals of the project, you'll have a productive discussion. If the designer can't explain their decisions, you're left with nothing but subjectivity to guide you, and you have nothing to give feedback on. Get them back in the room.

If push comes to shove and your designer cannot explain their decisions, you have a real problem—one that only gets more difficult as the project goes on.

The most important thing to keep in mind while evaluating design: what you're looking at isn't art, not even close. It's a business tool in the making and should be looked at objectively like any other business tool.

Your feedback for your designers is based on the same stuff you care about with any other person you interact with at work: how is this going to help your business succeed? That's something you are *very* good at evaluating.

The right question isn't "Do I like it?" but "Does this meet our goals?" If it's blue, don't ask yourself whether you like blue. Ask yourself if blue will help you sell sprockets. You just wrote your first feedback question.

Words you should never use in a design setting

No word is more useless in a design context than the word *like*. (Regardless of whether it's attached to a thumbs-up icon.) Million-dollar projects have been derailed by the word *like*. And many a cardboard box has been filled with personal items and walked to the front door by a disgruntled security guard because someone placed their bets on what someone liked.

Let's never use it again.

The problem with *like* is that it places the emphasis on success on someone's subjective mood rather than quantifiable data. When you hire me to do something, my job is to make sure it's successful. While I can't guarantee its success, I can significantly lessen the chances of failure by doing solid design research and making sure the work I do follows that research. But make no mistake, you're hiring me to make something succeed.

A good client knows the difference between personal opinion and goal-driven, informed evaluation.

I realize this may be hard for you to hear, but I honestly don't care whether you like what I do. (Don't throw the book across the room yet. Stick with me.) Obviously, if you like something, my job is easier. But what I can't do under any circumstances is make decisions based on whether you'll like them, instead of whether they'll succeed. And you honestly don't want me to.

Making you happy is never a project goal. If I'm focused on making you happy, I'm ignoring the real goals, and the project is more likely to fail. Are you still happy? (*Now* you can throw the book across the room. It's okay, you can buy another one.)

Let's face it. When we hear, "I like it," our minds go crazy and get filled with weird pheromones or something. (I'm making this up; I'm not a scientist.) We enjoy hearing it! We want to hear it again. It's human. And designers are human too, so we start doing work that gets you to say it again. Six months down the road when the project has failed and we're all wondering why, we won't get much relief from the fact that we all liked it. So let's not use it. Wean your designers from using it too. If your designer is trying to wean *you* from using it, well, this is why.

Try "This works" or "This seems correct" instead. Yeah I know, it's kinda dry. But it leads us to a better place. In the same vein, avoid words like *great, pretty,* and *happy.*

Screw feelings

I've had several wonderful clients who raved about the work for most of the project only to get to a point far along into implementation and decide the design was all wrong. God bless them. They were trying to spare my feelings. (Remember, I'm good with total honesty.) Sadly, they ended up tanking their budget and redoing a lot of work, which also meant missing their deadline.

Good feedback isn't synonymous with positive feedback. If something isn't working, tell the design team as early as possible. Will they be hurt? Not if they're professionals. A good designer will argue for their solution and know when to let go. (Note to designers: the time to let go is when it's clear that the solution isn't sufficiently effective, not as soon as a client expresses a negative personal opinion.)

Be respectful, but don't hold back to spare an individual's feelings. Taking criticism is part of the job description. The sooner your designers know, the sooner they can explore other paths. If you see something that you are absolutely, positively sure isn't going to work, and the designer hasn't convinced you otherwise, let them know. It's not going to grow on you. You're only going to get more irritated when you see it again.

Be direct

There's only one way to take, "This work sucks." There are many ways to take, "I'm not sure this is doing it for me." While the former may not be good feedback per se, it leaves no question that a problem needs addressing. Perhaps you can find a less blunt way to get your displeasure across, but don't do so at the cost of clarity. I'd rather have the clarity and I can deal with the bluntness, but I've been told I'm an asshole.

Lead with the general

Start with your summary evaluation. "Overall, this is going in the right direction." "Overall, this sucks." That sort of thing. Explain why and then go into detail. The why is the most important piece.

Don't bury the lede

We once got about ten pages of feedback from a client. It was incredibly detailed. Most of it was helpful (alongside a few prescriptive things): a good mix of questions about functionality, interface suggestions, workflow issues, and instances of places where we got stuff wrong.

We were pretty happy, because that level of detail generally means things are going in the right direction. Then, buried about two-thirds of the way down on page eight: "Overall, the design feels sterile."

No amount of tweaking will turn a potato into a schnauzer. If it doesn't work for you at a big-picture level, don't sweat the details. Get with your designer and hash it out.

Don't be prescriptive

Good feedback relates back to goals and user needs. Bad feedback is subjective and prescriptive. For example, "There's way too much going on here and the Add to Cart button gets lost," is excellent feedback. It relates to the page's goal, which is to apparently sell something, and communicates a problem to be solved, which is to get rid of the junk on the page.

Avoid personal preferences like, "I hate scrolling." I can do absolutely nothing with that statement. If research shows that your readers enjoy larger type and are comfortable scrolling, we're scrolling. You're not every reader. Building things to your own preferences makes one person happy: you. That's not enough people to make your site a success.

Prescriptive feedback is along the lines of: "Move the buttons over here." And everyone's favorite: "Make the logo bigger!" These may be decent ideas, but if we talked about the problems you're trying to solve with these prescriptive solutions, we may come up with better solutions or possibly uncover a larger problem in the design system.

It's akin to walking into your doctor's office and demanding a prescription for penicillin. You may need that, but there's no way you're walking out of that office without the pants coming down.

Don't try this at home

I've saved the worst feedback for the end (almost).

Nothing is less helpful than getting feedback in the form of a comp (whether committed in Photoshop, PowerPoint, or Word). Nothing. I mean it. We've been in business at Mule for almost ten years now, and this is the only thing we've ever fired a client over. (It happened once. The client refused to stop after we told them on numerous occasions that it was counterproductive, not to mention a contract violation.)

If something isn't working, point it out and go into as much detail as possible as to why. Tie it to the goals we agreed to earlier in the project. Understanding your reasoning is critical to solving the problem. Being told to do something a certain way, or worse, getting a comp of it done that way only means we have to reverse-engineer the whole thing and find out what you were trying to solve. Lost time. Lost budget.

Think of it this way. If a solution I came up with doesn't properly address your business goal and you're correcting me without saying why it's wrong, I'm going to remain ignorant of what's wrong. Which means I'm likely to keep doing it. Which means you're going to have to keep correcting me. That's a terrible way for you to spend your time.

Distill your feedback

"John in Sales wants to be able to log in directly on the homepage, but Tina in Engineering prefers it on its own page. Can we compromise?"

No. We cannot compromise.

If you tell your barber that you like it short but your significant other likes it long, you're gonna get a mullet.

Listen to your team's feedback, weigh the plusses and minuses, and then compile a clearly written document full of strong decisions. We can't design a solution to an internal debate. Nor should you pass that debate along for your customers to suffer through. If members of your team have varying ideas on something, iron it out. Invite your design team to join the debate. They should be eager as it informs their work. Reconciling feedback moves the process along. Sorting through ten pages of internal disagreement means lost time and budget.

Present your feedback

Just as we don't believe good design sells itself, we also don't believe good feedback explains itself. Set up a time to go over your feedback with your design team in person or on the phone. Walk through it together. Go over any sticking points, get clarity, and review issues that anyone on your team disagrees with. Bring that person on the call as well. The goal of this meeting is to make decisions and move forward.

Solid decisions, well communicated and well executed, are the path to success.

5 WHEN THINGS GO WELL

NO DESIGNER'S GONNA read your mind and get it right the first time, and you'll encounter the occasional stumbling block. (This is fine and normal, as long as you pay attention and get back on course.) But for the most part things should go well, and you'll see proof in the signs below. Some may be obvious; some may be counterintuitive.

REGULAR COMMUNICATION

The best sign that things are going well—or that you can fix things if they aren't—is having an open channel of communication. Whether they're in-house or outside designers, make sure they give you regular status reports and you can reach them when needed. Do you have a main contact on the design team? Establish one at the project's start. Who should you talk to if that person flakes on you? Have an escalation strategy ready. (Do this sparingly, if at all. You don't like it when people go over your head either.)

When we're on a project, it's almost guaranteed that someone on our team talks to someone on the client team every day. Steady communication ensures that any problem, no matter how small, is nipped in the bud before it has a chance to derail the project. It also keeps everyone informed on the project's progress and what they need to do their part. If you're handed a task, jump in. Otherwise, make sure everyone has access to the resources they need—and make sure they know who to go to if their access is blocked.

We get a little concerned if we can't reach a client for a couple of days, so I imagine they get concerned if they don't hear from us. Stay in the loop, and know what everyone is doing and why.

YOU MEET DEADLINES

An old client services proverb goes: "There's only one important deadline. The next one." Most clients have a specific date they need everything finished. We put together a project schedule that gets us to that final deadline, with several tiny ones before then.

Your deadlines are also part of that timeline. If you miss a deadline by three days, the entire project shifts by three days. (And if your designer has other work booked after yours, that extra time may not be there.)

Set appropriate deadlines at the project's beginning. You and the design team need to be honest about your ability to turn something around. Take vacation days, holidays, and company events into account. Keep the timeline realistic, not heroic.

PEOPLE ASK QUESTIONS

You hired someone to fix a complex problem within a complex organization. They better have some questions. More important, they better feel comfortable enough to ask those questions. If your design team is running around asking people on your team, yourself included, all kinds of questions, they're doing their job. That's the sound of people getting the information they need.

If your design team doesn't have any questions, you've got a problem. That's the sound of assumptions solidifying.

PEOPLE FORM RELATIONSHIPS

You know how I can tell when a project is going smoothly? When I see someone on my team and yours joking around on Twitter. Or going to lunch or getting a drink after work. These are signs that people get along and enjoy working with one another. Do you have to like each other to do good work together? No. You have to have respect. Absolutely. But man, it's so much easier when people enjoy working together. They're more open to other people's ideas and more supportive. You don't have weird ego crap. If someone screws up, they're willing to say so.

You can't force this. It either happens or it doesn't. But you can increase the odds by hiring people who are sociable, comfortable in their own skin, and confident in their abilities.

EVERY TIME YOUR DESIGNER SHOWS YOU SOMETHING, YOU UNDERSTAND WHY

Context. When the design team shows you something, do they tell you why they're doing this and what kind of feedback they need? That's good. It keeps the feedback focused on moving the project along. Which means you'll get it to them quicker and keep them moving toward the next milestone.

If they send you something with only a "What do you think of this?" attached, you have a problem. The question is too vague. It opens up too many possibilities.

Let me tell you a story that's happening all over the world between designers and clients. The designer sends something to the client, without any feedback guidelines. The client looks at it. They're unsure how to respond but want to do a thorough job. So they take a long time to write a longer email. The client hits send. The designer sighs and rolls his eyes. "I just wanted to know about the typeface." The design director asks, "Did you tell the client that?" The designer says, "Well, no." I swear to god this didn't *just* happen in my office this morning. I'm also not drinking right now.

THE WORK SLOWLY GETS BETTER

The proof is always in the pudding. Although the initial design concepts might've been rough and possibly off the mark (we talked about how this was okay, remember?), what you see afterward should be closer to being right with an extra level of refinement. You've been giving the team feedback. The team is iterating. Everyone is pushing each other to do something good. And everything is getting closer to the product that you'll eventually launch. There is no better feeling for a designer and a client to experience together.

PEOPLE ARGUE

Arguing is a good sign (in moderation). This means people give a shit. They're invested in what they're doing and passionate about the results. People who are disinterested don't argue. They meander from one task to another, making sure they do just enough so they don't get noticed. They go into checklist mode. They don't look for the best solution since any will do, as long as they get to check it off as done.

You don't want people throwing punches in the office. And you don't want the arguing to get personal. ("Your solution sucks" is okay. "You suck" is *not*.) Get them into a room and mediate. Figure out what they're arguing about and see if you can help them either find common ground or decide who's right. If they're arguing because they care about what they're doing, you've got it made.

PEOPLE TELL YOU THEY FUCKED UP

People fuck up in all sorts of exciting, interesting, and sometimes terrible ways. How is someone telling you they messed up a good sign? Because they're *telling* you. If you think your project is problem-free, it's because someone is hiding something.

When a designer tells you about something gone wrong, take a deep breath. Count how lucky you are. You've hired people who're willing to approach you about the problems they're having or causing. This gives you an opportunity to address them. You can fix zero of the problems you don't know about. You can fix some of the ones you *do*.

Also, pat yourself on the back for being the kind of person your team isn't afraid of talking to about the hard stuff.

THE DESIGNERS TRUST YOU ENOUGH TO SHOW YOU UNFINISHED WORK

It's one thing to show presentation-ready work. It's quite another to send out work that's broken and messy. Designers show each other unfinished stuff all the time. Usually because we wanna show off something clever we did, or we're stuck on solving a specific thing. But mostly we keep it to ourselves. Because we share a trade and it takes a certain amount of trust to share unfinished, messy work with a non-designer, especially the person who's paying you.

If a designer shows you work in progress, it's a great sign. It means they've moved beyond a fear that all you'll see is the broken stuff to a willingness to collaborate with you. Look at it in the spirit of collaboration. Ask questions about what they're showing. Talk about where they're headed with it. Feel free to ask if there's any feedback they're looking for at the moment. They've accepted you as part of the team that solves the problem.

You are now in the inner sanctum of sausage making. This is good.

YOU'VE SHOWN THE NEW SITE TO SOMEONE YOU WEREN'T SUPPOSED TO

Along the same lines, your designers will implore you not to show the site to anyone outside the company until it's ready. Why? Because a process exists to get this stuff done, and you agreed to follow it when you hired your designer—and look how far it's gotten you! I guarantee that fielding feedback from your nephew Dick, who took a graphics course in college, isn't part of that process. But the desire to share the work with Dick (and the rest of the world) because you're excited and want to show it off, is a good sign. Do it while he's asleep or something. We're excited that you're excited. Just don't give us Dick's feedback.

SOMEONE COMPLAINS ABOUT THE SORRY-ASS STATE OF YOUR LEGACY SYSTEMS

Shit is getting serious. If someone's complaining about legacy systems, that means they're deep in the weeds about to start the most heinous job in web services.

Dealing with legacy systems is like swimming through maple syrup. No one's legacy systems are in good shape. They've been cobbled and duct-taped together for years. The previous redesign probably entailed a quick fix to avoid them altogether. But at some point someone has to descend into the sub-basement of your website and pull this stuff out, clean it up, and import it into shiny, new systems.

The people dealing with your legacy systems are like that person in horror movies who's brave enough to go into the storm cellar by themselves with nothing but a whiffle bat and a box of kitchen matches, while the rest of the team peeks from behind the door at the top of the steps. They'll root around in databases containing names from the Mayflower expedition. They'll sift through years of content and delete inline styles. They'll collapse more tables than the caterers after a royal wedding. Treat them like the heroes they are and make sure they have pizza and beer and big bonuses at the end.

Please, for the love of all that's holy, don't farm this out to someone to do in their spare time. This shit is hard and time-consuming, and if you ignore it until the last minute, your project *will* fail.

Which is why we're happy that people started early. It's a very good sign indeed.

YOUR TEAM IS EXCITED ABOUT THE NEXT DELIVERABLE

People settle into one of three emotional camps during a design project:

- Hatred
- Indifference
- Excitement

I almost added anxiety as a fourth, but decided you could be anxious no matter what camp you're in.

If the people in your company are excited about what's going on and can't wait to see what happens next, that's awesome. Even better is if they participate and seek out ways to get involved. This means they've taken a stake in the project's health and will work their butts off to ensure its success.

PEOPLE STAY LATE TO WORK

I threw this in here to trip you up. I've worked in several companies where staying late was viewed as a good sign. If you left at a reasonable time, you were a traitor to the cause. There will always be moments during the project, notably toward the end, where people have to rally to meet a deadline. When this happens, and it should be infrequent, bring them food and stay out of their hair. If it starts happening regularly, something is screwed up. Take a look at your timelines to see if they're unreasonable. Get a history of deadlines and see how many have been missed. Talk to the project manager. Long working hours aren't a sign of a project going well or of devotion to the company. They're a sign that something has gone wrong. Everyone deserves to go home at a reasonable hour.

THE CURRENT SITE MAKES YOU SICK

You knew the old site had problems, or you wouldn't have brought in designers to fix it. But as your new site takes shape, you're going to look at your current site like a box of week-old donuts you can't wait to trash. If you find yourself debating whether the new site is better than the old site, that's a problem. But that moment when you pull up the old site and throw up in your mouth a bit? That's a good sign.

YOU DIDN'T MIND WRITING THAT LAST CHECK

No one likes writing a check if they don't feel like they've gotten that check's value. But we're generally happy to exchange money for something we feel is worth it. Same with design projects. When the desire to get more of the project done beats the desire to hang onto your money, the project is going well.

YOU WANT TO POACH SOMEONE ON THE DESIGN TEAM

Someone on the design team may do such incredible work, get along with everyone on your team, and understand your business *so* well that you're inclined to think, "Boy, I sure wish they worked for us."

Hey, that's great. We want you to feel that way about everyone on the design team. Our goal is to become indispensable to the point that you couldn't imagine working with anybody else. We want you to be sad that we'll eventually leave.

Wanting to poach someone from the design team is a good sign. Actually doing so is a whole different beast. Let's all agree to dance with the one that brung us.

But we're honored you'd want to.

YOUR BOSS IS HAPPY

Let me tell you the happiest type of email I get. It comes from the project lead a few months after the project launches. It's some variation of: "Hey, wanted to let you know how well the project was received. Our numbers are up and users are overjoyed. Oh, and on a personal note, I got a promotion!"

Nothing makes me happier than finding out the person who put their trust in us and stuck with us through the work's duration, ended up looking good and getting recognized for that decision.

One of the designer's goals is making the person who hired them look like a genius. So I do what I can to support that person when their boss is breathing down their neck. Obviously, this starts with doing good work. But it also means keeping to the timeline, staying within budget, communicating clearly, and offering to stand side-by-side with them when they get called upstairs.

When the people upstairs are happy, the project goes better, you have the room to do your work, and everyone's a little less anxious.

YOU HAVE A CLEAR PATH TO THE FINISH LINE

At the very beginning of the project, you and your design team should define what "done" means. Is it launching the site? Turning over a certain set of deliverables? Passing through QA testing without any bugs? Those are all fine and valid, as long as both parties agree.

When you can see the finish line ahead of you with no further obstacles in your path, you're gold. Take those few extra steps, cross that line, and celebrate. You are now done. Pop the corks, sign the checks, and await the inevitable promotions.

No, you still can't poach anyone.

SUMMING IT UP

These are all signs the project is going well. No project is perfect, but knowing how to gauge its health will help you catch mistakes early enough to rectify them without losing too much time or momentum.

But what happens when mistakes don't get caught, or when partnerships go sour, or you find that, despite your best efforts, you made the wrong choices and they're unrecoverable? Sadly, it happens. (Hopefully reading this book will minimize the odds of it happening.) Let's talk about what to do in the worst-case scenarios.

6 WHEN THINGS GO WRONG

Despite everyone's best efforts, people make mistakes. How do you sort the small ones from the big ones? How do you know when to change course or cut the cord?

How many of you skipped right to this chapter? It's okay. If you're knee-deep in a project that isn't going well, I can help. First, take a deep breath. Let's do some triage. We'll cover whether you're looking at small or big mistakes. If they're large, we'll go over whether you can fix them. Sometimes you can.

After thoroughly exhausting our options, we'll knock some heads.

SIGNS THINGS ARE GOING WRONG

In the last chapter, we talked about how to tell if the project was going well. Reverse those things, and you've got signs that it *isn't:* the designer doesn't communicate with you. It's been so long since you've seen them that you forgot what they looked like. They don't return your calls or emails. Their work gets worse. They're missing deadlines, and you have someone breathing down your neck, because everything rests on your shoulders and you're freaking out that you may have hired the wrong people.

It happens. Sometimes, despite everyone's best intentions, projects go wrong. Sometimes, despite everyone doing their due diligence, they hire the wrong people. *Sometimes,* and you're gonna like this part, you can fix these things. Sometimes you can't. Let's figure out the difference.

BIG VERSUS SMALL MISTAKES

Starting a kitchen fire is a small mistake. If you've prepared properly and have a fire extinguisher nearby, you can put it out. Running away and letting the house burn down is a big mistake.

Mistakes happen on every single project, at every point during the project. You can't avoid them. You shouldn't even try. Okay, you should try a little. But the case I'm trying to make is that you're better off putting your energy in figuring out how to recover from mistakes than avoiding them altogether.

A small mistake happens when someone gets the number of templates wrong, forgets to add some obscure functionality, or delivers feedback on Thursday morning instead of Wednesday afternoon. Anything you can fix with a few hours or even days of work is a small mistake. No biggie. You settle up and do the extra work, adjust the project timeline, and move on. The person who made the mistake will likely be extra attentive from now on, which is good, because you'll watch them like a hawk for a bit to make sure they learned their lesson.

The thing that turns a small mistake into a big one is failing to acknowledge it. I hope you're basketball fans. If you played as a kid, one of the very first things your coach should have taught you is the minute you get whistled for committing a foul, you raise your hand. You own that mistake. The other team takes their free throws and everyone moves on. I have no patience whatsoever for someone who can't acknowledge making a mistake, especially since I've done a pretty good job of letting people know that mistakes are part of the process. People who can't admit their errors are usually afraid. They're worried they'll be judged and thought less of. You need to create an environment where this isn't the case. Someone who acknowledges their mistakes is a good person to have around. Not only do they own their responsibilities, but you can be fairly sure they're not hiding anything from you. A small mistake that isn't uncovered can grow into a large one.

A big mistake is something that puts the project timeline at risk. It's one thing to forget to add social tools to the site. That's fixed in a few hours. It's quite another to revisit a decision made three months ago. That's major. It means that any decision made after the mistake is up in the air—and may mean losing hours and budget, and putting the final deadline in jeopardy.

If your design team is internal, that extra time is easier to find. If the mistake rests solidly on the design firm's shoulders, they need to fix it and eat the time and budget. But if the mistake's on both of you, as is often the case, or if you're the one with the hand in the air, you may have to deal with the reality that they've already booked another project after yours.

Avoid mistakes of this magnitude by frequently checking in, paying attention to details, and taking extra care that sign-off really means sign-off. Cross your t's and dot your i's.

I can't stress this enough: never, ever, ever sign off on work without being absolutely confident in your decision. Make sure that anyone who can undo that decision gives the green light. It's better to spend a few extra days doing your due diligence than run the risk of having a project undone because someone who needed to be consulted wasn't.

HOW DO YOU KNOW IT'S UNRECOVERABLE?

The minute your goals shift from doing good work to salvaging current work, you have a problem. You've compromised your standard of quality. Even if the project recovers, your relationship with the design team may not. In fact, the key to the project's viability may be to get the design team as far away as possible.

The levels of project quality expectations, in descending order:

- We're going to do amazing work
- We're going to do pretty good work
- We're going to get this out the door
- We're going to cover our ass
- We can probably spin this on our résumé

When you get down to those last two, you're in the middle of an irreversible mistake—the type that needs a project reset. You're definitely on your way to an unpleasant conversation with your design team and, if you have one, your boss.

How do you know the relationship is unrecoverable? Simple. You no longer trust the designers. If you don't believe your team is capable of doing good work, you've lost trust in them. They have to go. Here's the sad dark secret. It may not be fair. You may no longer trust your team for reasons that are totally unfair to them. You may be the one who screwed up. You may be scapegoating them. (In which case they no longer trust you either.) The goal is to be able to work together, not assign blame. If you've decided you can't work together anymore, it's time to part ways. Bear in mind, deciding you need to get rid of a team because you've scapegoated them and they no longer trust you may be the right thing to do for the sake of the project. It still makes you a jerk. But a jerk who's getting the project done.

Let me tell you a story. We were working on this project for a company we (still) admire. Good work. Fun team. It was their first time hiring an outside firm to do their design work. We were doing good work. The problem was, whenever we showed work to their CEO, who fancied himself a designer (biggest red flag in the business), his only reaction was, "This doesn't feel like us. Why aren't we doing this work internally?" No matter what we showed him, that was the reaction. We were obviously in a situation where the client didn't trust us. To be fair, it had nothing to do with us, and the rest of the team trusted us fine. I saw no way past this, other than letting them kill the project and do it internally. And I was very grateful when they fired us at our request. The project never launched, by the way.

THE COME-TO-JESUS MEETING

Sometimes things are worth saving, and you gotta give it one last shot. That's the basis of the come-to-Jesus meeting. This isn't a fun meeting. It's the last chance. Your job is to walk a tightrope between communicating the situation's severity and leaving people feeling empowered enough to take advantage of the opportunity you so graciously gave them.

One rule: never make people think they have a chance when they don't. If you've decided to get rid of them, just do so. A fake last chance is a bullshit move that costs you more time and money. Not to mention that it's totally unfair to the people who you obviously don't trust anymore and need to go get a fresh start somewhere else. Never punish people or cover your ass by making them think they have another chance.

If the team has strayed so far off course that the project is spiraling toward failure, get everyone in a room and let them know. I recommend a direct approach. Something like, "You've strayed off course and the project is headed toward failure!"

Don't beat around the bush. This isn't one of those "let's see if they come to the same conclusion" meetings.

Once you have their attention, lay out the severity of the situation, including the consequences. I recommend rewatching the Alec Baldwin "Coffee is for closers" speech from *Glengarry Glen Ross* to psych yourself up. (Check YouTube.) Once they understand what's at stake, you either present your plan for moving forward or workshop that plan together, should you still trust them to do so. However you do it, they need to understand that the minute they walk out of this meeting, their job is to execute that plan. No arguments, no bullshit.

Don't promise anything beyond that. You may not have the power to do so. Even if they manage to pull the project out of the toilet, they're still the team that dumped it there.

You're absolutely right. These meetings aren't fun. You know what's even less fun? Explaining to your boss, investors, and other employees who aren't part of this project but are nevertheless affected by it that you failed. *This* meeting is your last chance to avoid *that* meeting.

COMMUNICATING FAILURE

It's neither easy nor enjoyable to tell someone they've failed. Only one thing's worse: making someone feel like they've succeeded when they haven't. Failure is an opportunity for growth and learning.

If I've failed at something, and that failure has been confirmed by the person who hired me to accomplish the task, I have a decision to make. Either I can be a dick and get defensive about the situation, and claim that I didn't fail, or I can acknowledge that I failed. If I take the former option, I learn nothing, and I gain a reputation as a terrible person to work with. If I take the latter, I can review my actions, look for where I screwed up, and ask my boss for details or advice. I can use it as an opportunity to get better at what I do by not repeating those mistakes. I also come off as a person who knows how to hop back on a horse after being thrown.

As the person communicating that failure, it's in your best interest, especially if you have a long-term relationship with this designer, to set the conversation up to get the result you want. I can help you with a few guidelines. The first and most important is to do this in person whenever possible.

Never communicate angry

It's completely valid to be pissed off when someone on your team fucks up. Walk it off. Telling someone they fucked up when you're furious guarantees you put them on the defensive. Which I can almost guarantee you'll react to by saying, "Don't get defensive!" and then everything goes nuclear and everyone is screaming.

Have a plan

What will you say? In what order? What outcome do you want? Have you already made a decision about their future? Are you going to decide during the meeting? If you're giving them a second chance, what do those steps look like?

Know the outcome you want

If you're set on canning this person, skip ahead. But if you're giving them a second (or third) chance, make sure you clearly communicate the steps they need to take and the evidence you need to see before you give them another shot.

Realize that you're taking it upon yourself to help them through that period. Give them clear goals, set up regular check-ins, and make sure they can come to you when they need to. Their success or failure is now intricately tied to yours.

Read the room

Even if you've decided to give this person a second chance, give yourself enough time with them to see whether they're able to accept it. Walk them through what happened. Ask them to explain their process and the decisions that went into it. If they're taking ownership of their mistakes, go ahead and give them that second chance. But if you're hearing a lot of blame shifted around and a lot of coworkers thrown under the bus, keep that second chance in your back pocket. The bottom line here is whether you can trust this person again. Sometimes, sadly, people are their own worst enemies.

FIRING A DESIGNER

A designer's main priority is the project they're designing. No one should put themselves above it. Since you're leading that project, your responsibility is to the health of the work and the team doing the work. When someone doesn't do their job, they put an undue stress on those around them. When you don't do anything about that undue stress, morale tanks.

Getting fired should never come as a surprise. If someone's not working out, you need to let them know. You should tell them how they need to improve and by when. If they take it as a wake-up call, they'll be forever grateful that you gave them a chance. If you don't see any progress, or they do an even worse job after that conversation, cut 'em loose.

Trust me, someone who's in above their head knows it. Firing them will not be a surprise. You're probably doing them the favor of not having to come in and go through the motions. (And, no, this is not a way for you to feel good about firing someone.)

I've fired a few designers in my time, and they've gone off to have great careers. I've been fired myself more than once, and here I am talking to you. Getting fired isn't the end of the world; it's the end of a job.

Let's be clear about this: firing someone sucks. It *should* suck. The fact that you feel terrible about it is a sign you're actually a human being. But however much it may suck to fire someone, it doesn't come close to how much it sucks to get fired.

Doing the right thing doesn't always feel great. That doesn't mean it's not the right thing to do.

I am far from an HR professional, and your company may have its own guidelines for firing people. But I do encourage you to do it with as much clarity and honesty and empathy as possible. Someone who's getting fired deserves to know why they're getting fired, no matter what your HR department says.

WHAT ABOUT YOUR MONEY?!?

Oh right. Money's on the table. If this person is your employee, it's routine. Last paycheck, plus unused vacation time, yadda, yadda, yadda. If you're in a large company, there's a process for dealing with it, so you don't even need to think about it.

If you've hired a designer from the outside, things get more complicated. Except that they *really* don't. You pay people for the work they did. This is exactly the kind of situation that should be addressed in the contract you both signed before you started the project, specifically in the kill fee. But as a general guideline, you most definitely owe people for the work you've approved. If they did good work for two-thirds of the project and you signed off on it and paid them, that money is gone.

I can hear you saying, "But it ended up failing."

I feel your pain. I do. But the fact that you signed off on stuff means that you were satisfied and acknowledged that things were proceeding in a good way. Make sure you are clear about what you are signing off on and the ramifications. It's going to be very difficult for you to go back and try to convince the design team or your boss that you signed off on work that was headed toward failure. You're going to have to convince someone that the design team was keeping something from you, that they knew failure was imminent, and that you signed off on work under false pretenses. If you actually believe that to be the case, then by all means proceed. I have no love for design firms that swindle their clients. It makes everyone in the business look bad, and it makes my job harder. It's just not going to be an easy case to make.

If the design team comes back and says that you owe them for time and work that was in progress, that's trickier. Once again, this is something that should be addressed in the contract. And once again, I have a very simple guideline: if you're going to use the work, even after firing them, pay them for it. But if you're not using the work, well, fuck 'em.

Like I said, I have no patience for design firms that make us all look bad.

RECONSTRUCTION

Let's not end on a bad note. After all, we still have a project to complete. Even if we've fired the design team. Time to pick up the pieces, take inventory of our situation, and figure out where to go from here.

The first thing we need to determine is whether we can finish the project without a designer. We're entering dangerous waters. To do this, the project needs to be pretty far along, with major systems defined, and the site well into implementation. *Well* into implementation.

Ask yourself: can you finish the project without a designer and preserve the quality of the final project? Don't make your users pay for the designer's mistake. Your users deserve the best you can give them. Don't rush to completion if you're going to deliver a substandard product. You may win a battle to lose the war.

If you find yourself in need of another designer, some trust-building exercises may be in order. You just went through a

FIG 3: Firing someone is never fun. Here's a unicorn chaser. Photograph by Rob Boudon (http://bkaprt.com/ymfc/7/).

shitty experience with a designer and it's important that you rebuild your trust in design.

Before searching for someone new, take stock of what you've learned. Did you miss a red flag during hiring? Did the problem stem from the quality of the work or the relationship? Do you need someone with more experience? Or did you choose the cheapest option over someone more qualified because you wanted to save money? (Guess what? You didn't save money. What you save on cost, you take on risk.)

I can always tell when a client comes to us after a bad experience with another designer. They're still feeling the sting of being ripped off. Rightfully so. Their questions tend to be pointed—a vapor trail to their pain. Which is good, because I can speak to that pain and help them feel at ease about working with a designer again.

What I need you to remember, though, is that the next designer you hire isn't responsible for what happened with your previous one. Don't make your new designer pay for your old designer's sins. Transference is not in scope. A new designer starts with a clean slate. You're handing them one hell of a hot potato.

Look, anyone you bring in at this point is going to need some time to get acquainted with the project. They'll be able to assess how much of it needs to be redone and how quickly it can happen. Make sure the designer you're bringing in isn't redoing it for the sake of putting their own mark on it. Yes, had they been there from the beginning, they would have made different decisions. But this is where we are now. Don't forget: design solves a problem within a set of constraints. Tell them one of yours is that you have a half-finished project that needs an honest evaluation of how much is worth keeping. Possibly add an incentive—offer them a bonus if they finish by a certain date. (You'll be amazed how much of that work is now salvageable!)

Most projects go well if you hire the right person for the job, work collaboratively, and communicate frequently. But even with the best of intentions, projects sometimes go south. Get out of those situations as quickly as possible. Assess the damage. Come up with a plan to move forward. Don't let one bad experience destroy your confidence in good design and the people who do it.

Remember, saving a few bucks often ends up costing you far more.

CONCLUSION

"I don't know anything about design."

You can't say that! Armed with the information in this book, you can judge who you're hiring by qualities you understand. You'll look for designers who behave like professionals. You and your design team will communicate with each other better than ever, and you'll trust your designers to do their job to the best of their abilities.

Most of all, you can make sure that the money your organization spends on design is spent well.

Does reading this book guarantee smooth sailing in your design endeavors? Nope, not by a long shot. Because we're dealing with people. Infuriating, infuriating people. But the stuff you've picked up means that you can plot a course to avoid those rough patches by knowing the right questions to ask potential designers and red flags to look for. Work with designers with confidence, because when things go wrong, you'll know what to do.

When I told a friend that I was thinking of writing this book, he asked, "Why would clients trust a designer telling them how to work with other designers? After all, you're one of them." A fantastic question, which made me hate him for a couple of days until I figured out the answer: I'm more frustrated by the way some designers behave than you are. I do this for a living. My welfare depends on people understanding the value of design and being willing to work with the people who make it. Every designer who pulls a diva routine puts my welfare at risk.

Don't get me wrong. Many, many wonderful designers out there in the world do good work. They won't all be right for you. But I hope this book helps you find those who are and establish long, fruitful, mutually beneficial relationships.

Finally, thank you for reading and trusting me with your time.

GLOSSARY

Designers use certain words time and again in the design process. Since we use them every day, we may not always remember to explain them to you (though we should). If you're working with a designer and they mention something you aren't familiar with, don't hesitate to ask them to clarify. If their eyes light up at the prospect of explaining it, you're working with the right people.

I've taken the liberty of defining terms I've neglected to explain to clients in the past. This isn't an exhaustive list, but I hope it's helpful.

agile — A process for design and development that values speed and prototyping above documentation. It works great for small product teams and less so with outside agencies who deliver work to others for final implementation. Ironically, a lot of documentation exists on how to work this way. Whatever process you go with, hire people who work fast and enjoy making things.

artifact — Things made throughout the project that aren't deliverables (for example, Photoshop files). Personally, I work out concepts and the first few simple layouts in Photoshop. Once we've sorted out major decisions, our team moves into code, where we make tons of adjustments that we don't reflect back in Photoshop. Those Photoshop files are artifacts; they helped us get to our final deliverable, code.

When you ask if you can have the Photoshop files, the answer is yes. After all, we made them on your dime. (Other studios' policies may differ.) But don't expect them to mirror the final work.

budget — What we've agreed the work is worth. Work requested after that agreement requires extra budget and depends on the designer's availability. (Unless of course you control the designer's time.)

comp or mockup — Comp is short for *comprehensive layout*. (Now you know something your designer probably doesn't.) A comp shows the final placement of objects on the page or screen. Think of it as a painting of a website. It's the fleshed-out version of the concept and should start resembling the final thing (it isn't real until it's coded). *Mockup* is also acceptable. *Mock* is not. I mean, c'mon.

concept — An idea. Before your designer spends time diddling with little interface elements burning through hours, they should put something in front of you that illustrates a basic idea. They should also talk you through where it *could* go.

content — Content is every possible reason someone comes to your website: the writing, videos, stuff in your databases, pants you have for sale, photos, plane tickets, etc. Design's job is to make content easy to find and present it in the best light possible.

deadline — When things are due. A project is a series of deadlines. You'll have some, the designer'll have some. Everybody knows the project's final deadline, which also is the least important. The *most* important deadline is the next one. Because if you miss it, you miss all the ones after.

deliverable — The thing you get at the end of this whole process. While your site or app may be your *final* deliverable, you'll have interim deliverables throughout the project. Remember that the interim deliverables are important for two reasons: they inform the final deliverable, and they help gain stakeholders' approval. Don't ignore that second one. We've made many a wireframe or comp presentation to the CEO to alleviate their anxiety mid-project.

discovery — What some design studios call a project's research phase (us included). Because we discover things. Sometimes things you don't want us to.

feedback — Constructive response to the thing you see. Feedback can be positive or negative. "I don't understand what you're trying to do here" is also helpful. Both clients and designers should give feedback during the design process. A designer giving you feedback on a decision you're making is totally fair game.

iteration — Nobody gets it right the first time. With helpful feedback from you, the designer gets closer with every step. Iteration is part of the process; that things get better incrementally with your feedback is a feature not a flaw.

prescriptive feedback — Also known as trying to do the designer's job. "Move this twenty pixels to the left" isn't feedback. Prescriptive feedback hinders a designer's ability to do their job as they spend the next three hours figuring out the actual problem you're trying to solve.

prototype — A quick and dirty version of the design used for testing or convincing the client that an idea has legs. Also called a *proof of concept.* Thrown away after the point is made.

responsive design — A design solution that allows one codebase to work across platforms: desktop, tablets, and mobile. This means you don't need to maintain multiple versions of your site, which is a good thing. Responsive design optimizes a site's layout based on your device. When your designer presents you with the first bits of a coded site, they'll sit there expanding and shrinking the browser window so you see the page's elements rearrange themselves. Your designer will keep doing it even after you've gotten the idea.

scope — The amount of work everyone has agreed the project entails. Once you've agreed to the scope, you can't increase it without revisiting the budget and deadlines.

spec work — Short for *speculative work*. This means asking your designer to do the work first, with payment dependent on getting the work approved. Which is like agreeing to pay your therapist only if you stop doing terrible things like asking designers to work on spec.

waterfall — A linear process where each team finishes their part of the project in its entirety before handing it to the next team. For example, the visual designers make 300 Photoshop files and dump them with the front-end developers, who are probably seeing that work for the first time. This is like the telephone game, where the first person whispers, "Potato," and three people later, it's "You walk the dog. I'm trying to finish my book." Waterfall's biggest problem is the amount of knowledge lost between phases as you have little to no collaboration.

wireframe — A blueprint of the stuff needed on any particular screen or page. It's usually a bunch of boxes with annotations. The person who shows them (e.g., an interaction designer or information architect) will make a big deal about how a wireframe doesn't imply layout, even though things are totally laid out. A good designer sees past the layout and moves elements around as needed. There isn't an industry standard for making wireframes, so they can be as simple as a sketch on a whiteboard or complex and carefully designed objects in their own right. But if your design team spends their time prettifying wireframes, they're wasting your money.

RESOURCES

A Book Apart

This book has a circle with the number twelve on the cover, because it's part of a library started a few years ago by good people who wanted to help out designers. The books are short, so you can get back to work. This one is the first written specifically for clients, but you may enjoy the others as well. I've already mentioned *Just Enough Research* by Erika Hall and *The Elements of Content Strategy* by Erin Kissane. You should also pick these up:

- *Design Is a Job,* Mike Monteiro (Yeah, I'm gonna be a dick and mention my own book first. This is a handbook for designers on how to approach their job in a way that benefits both designers and clients. Buy it for every designer on your team. Read it too. It's as funny as this one, and it has a different picture of me.)
- *Content Strategy for Mobile,* Karen McGrane (More and more of your customers are using mobile devices to get to your stuff. Mobile isn't the future; it's here now. This book teaches you how to plan, organize, and adapt your content across devices.)
- *Responsive Web Design,* Ethan Marcotte (Save time, money, and stress by making one site that accommodates any device. You've been delivered: no more keeping track of your desktop and mobile sites.)
- *On Web Typography,* Jason Santa Maria (Experts like to say that nobody reads on the web. They're wrong, but truth be told, reading on the web in the early days suuuuuuucked. We had limited access to good fonts, and type was tiny. That's all changed. Things are delightful now. Everyone should read more.)

The other titles are also very good, but they get nerdier and contain more code. If you're comfortable in that arena, take a look at the entire library at A Book Apart (http://bkaprt.com/ymfc/8/).

If you have designers in house, buy the whole set. Buy my book twice.

Understanding design

- *Go: A Kidd's Guide to Graphic Design,* Chip Kidd (Pay no attention to the title. This book isn't just for kids. Chip Kidd explains the principles of graphic design in a clear, effective, and delightful manner like no one else. Young and old will appreciate it.)

Making websites and other stuff

- *Don't Make Me Think: A Common Sense Approach to Web Usability,* Steve Krug (A well-written, concise, and humorous book on how to design websites for human beings. Common sense is right in the name. I've recommended this book to clients since it first came out.)
- *Designing for the Digital Age: How to Create Human-Centered Products and Services,* Kim Goodwin (Clocking in at 768 pages, this isn't light reading for the faint of heart, but it does have everything you need. I believe the word is comprehensive. If nothing else, you can throw the book at your designer's head.)

Working with others

- *Designing Together: The Collaboration and Conflict Management Handbook for Creative Professionals,* Dan Brown (No, not that Dan Brown. This Dan Brown has run a design shop called EightShapes for a while and doesn't have time for that shit. He's also an expert in getting people to work together.)
- *Steve Jobs,* Walter Isaacson (There will only ever be one Steve Jobs. Read this to find out how he behaved. If your designer starts exhibiting any of the same traits, fire them. Because they are not, nor will they ever be, Steve Jobs.)

Thinking creatively

- *Steal Like an Artist* and *Show Your Work!*, Austin Kleon. (Creative is a great adjective and a shitty noun. All of us, no matter what we do for a living, could use more creativity in our lives. These books, available everywhere, including Walgreens, will show you that creativity is not a random event, but a process to work toward.)

Writing RFPs

RFPs are the devil. Go back and read the section about RFPs if you don't believe me. But your organization may require you to write one. For the love of Pete, don't write one unless you absolutely have to, but if you do, here are some tips:

- RFPs: Help Us Help You, Rawle Anders: http://bkaprt.com/ymfc/9/
- How RFP Timelines Can Sabotage Your Redesign, Matt Simmons: http://bkaprt.com/ymfc/10/
- RFP Advice from the Front Lines, Joe Rinaldi: http://bkaprt.com/ymfc/11/
- How to Write an Effective Website Design RFP, Flynt Johnson: http://bkaprt.com/ymfc/12/

ACKNOWLEDGEMENTS

A very special thank you to the good people at A Book Apart. Jeffrey, who I hope is over his cold soon. Jason, who keeps it all looking sharp. Katel, who makes the trains run on time. And Tina Lee, who waded through a lot of words to find the good ones. Thank you for agreeing to follow me to a second location. Few would.

A huge thank you to Mandy Brown for her encouragement in getting this book off the ground.

This book wouldn't be possible without my past, present, and future clients. People who could've chosen to work with anyone yet chose to work with me. I know how hard it can be to get those budgets approved and stars lined up, and I know your asses are on the line. I don't take that for granted. I am forever grateful to you all for putting your trust in me and my company.

A special thank you to Kevin Cosgrove and Andrew Anker, two clients kind enough to proofread the book from the intended reader's point of view.

To everyone past and present at Mule Design, where I get to learn something new from somebody every day.

To the usual gang of miscreants who put up with me. Ross Floate. Jennifer Daniel. Andre Torrez and Amber Costley. Caleb Sexton. Ryan Carver and Rae Brune. Bryan Mason, to whom I owe $200. Jeff Veen, who'll forever buy my drinks. Amy Jane and John Gruber, who extended their hospitality. Dan Sinker, who loves goats. Jessie Char, my cohost. Miranda Mulligan. Kristina Halvorson. Jeff Wishnie. Karen McGrane. Ethan Marcotte. Jared Spool and Dana Chisnell, whose insight and generosity know no bounds. Ryan Freitas. Tim Buckwalter. Karen Wickre, who secretly runs everything. Jeff Tidwell, who climbs mountains with me. Andrew Crow, who keeps big companies honest. Colleen Wainwright, who is my spirit animal. To Tash and Mike for allowing me on their stage. To Mike Essl and Mia Eaton for moving across the country. To the Gregs for being role models of craft and kindness. To my lawyer, Gabe Levine, who keeps me on the good side of right.

A special thank you to David McCreath for putting up with my shit longer than anybody.

To Tina Belcher, who writes the best fan fiction.

To my parents, Americo and Judite Monteiro, who taught me the value of hard work.

To Annette Rankin, who works harder than any of you can imagine. And gets results.

To my son, Henry, who does things at seventeen that I never had the courage to do. May history someday remember me only as Henry Monteiro's father.

To my wife, Erika Hall, who was raised by strong-ass women and doesn't take shit from anybody.

To every woman in design and tech who puts up with bullshit every day and refuses to give up.

To everyone who ever lost their job fighting for good design.

And to Anil Dash, who skipped right to this page.

REFERENCES

Shortened URLs are numbered sequentially; the related long
URLs are listed below for reference.

Chapter 1

1 http://commons.wikimedia.org/wiki/File:1968_El_Camino.jpg
2 http://www.uie.com/articles/design_rendering_intent/
3 http://www.propublica.org/
4 https://twitter.com/jmspool/status/391311660062736384

Chapter 2

5 http://nest.com

Chapter 3

6 http://simpsons.wikia.com/wiki/The_Homer

Chapter 6

7 https://www.flickr.com/photos/robboudon/6035265163/in/photostream/

Resources

8 http://www.abookapart.com
9 http://muledesign.com/2013/11/rfps-help-us-help-you/
10 http://www.insidenewcity.com/blog/view/how-rfp-timelines-can-sabotage-
    your-redesign
11 http://cognition.happycog.com/article/rfp-advice-from-the-front-lines
12 http://www.gravitatedesign.com/blog/how-to-write-rfp-website-design/

INDEX

R

S

T

V

ABOUT A BOOK APART

We cover the emerging and essential topics in web design and development with style, clarity, and above all, brevity—because working designer-developers can't afford to waste time.

COLOPHON

The text is set in FF Yoga and its companion, FF Yoga Sans, both by Xavier Dupré. Headlines and cover are set in Titling Gothic by David Berlow.

This book was printed in the United States using FSC certified Finch papers.